# A Few Buttons Missing

# A
# Few Buttons Missing

*The Case Book of a Psychiatrist*

JAMES T. FISHER, M.D.
*and*
LOWELL S. HAWLEY

J. B. LIPPINCOTT COMPANY
PHILADELPHIA AND NEW YORK

# CONTENTS

*Foreword*                                                          7

1  *The training of children is a profession, where we must
   know how to lose time in order to gain it.*—ROUSSEAU        11

2  *We go by the major vote, and if the majority are insane,
   the sane must go to the hospital.*—H. MANN                 23

3  *I am a part of all that I have met.*—TENNYSON              32

4  *Seems it strange that thou shouldst live forever? Is it less
   strange that thou shouldst live at all?—This is a miracle: and
   that no more.*—YOUNG                                       44

5  *It is with disease of the mind, as with those of the body:
   we are half dead before we understand our disorder, and half
   cured when we do.*—COLTON                                  55

6  *Indigestion is charged by God with enforcing morality on
   the stomach.*—HUGO                                         66

7  *It is indeed a desirable thing to be well descended, but the
   glory belongs to our ancestors.*—PLUTARCH                  81

8  *The true test of civilization is, not the census, nor the size
   of cities, nor the crops, but the kind of man that the country
   turns out:*—EMERSON                                        96

9  *What mean ye, fellow citizens, that ye turn every stone to
   scrape wealth together, and take so little care of your children,
   to whom ye must one day relinquish all?*—SOCRATES         110

10 *He who reigns within himself and rules his passions, desires and fears is more than a king.*—MILTON 127

11 *It is the little rift within the lute that by and by will make the music mute, and ever widening slowly silence all.* —TENNYSON 137

12 *The excesses of our youth are drafts upon our old age, payable with interest about thirty years after date.*—COLTON 153

13 *Everything that exceeds the bounds of moderation, has an unstable foundation.*—SENECA 165

14 *Sometimes we may learn more from a man's errors, than from his virtues.*—LONGFELLOW 174

15 *Sit in reverie, and watch the changing color of the waves that break upon the idle seashore of the mind.* —LONGFELLOW 189

16 *We may take fancy for a companion, but must follow reason as our guide.*—SAMUEL JOHNSON 207

17 *The years teach much which the days never know.* —EMERSON 224

18 *True, I talk of dreams, which are the children of an idle brain, begot of nothing but vain fantasy.*—SHAKESPEARE 237

19 *Men of age object too much, consult too long, adventure too little, repent too soon.*—FRANCIS BACON 254

20 *Men will wrangle for religion; write for it; fight for it; die for it; anything but live for it.*—COLTON 269

# FOREWORD

AN AUTOBIOGRAPHY, LIKE the automotive "one-man top" of an earlier era, lends itself readily to the combined efforts of two or more people. And I see no reason why dual authorship on such a story as this should require any special explanation or apology.

I am, I believe, one of the few laymen who has ever sat quietly taking notes and asking questions, while the psychiatrist lay on the couch giving voice to his thoughts at random.

The story that follows is Dr. Fisher's story. It is the story of his life and of his experiences. And to some extent, I hope, it portrays his philosophy. It seems entirely logical to me that it should be related in the first person.

Case histories have been included for illustrative purposes only. Names, initials, and incidents have been disguised to avoid identification of, or embarrassment to, former patients. As all case histories are reasonably typical, they may present some similarity to cases that have received Dr. Fisher's attentions through the years, but this is coincidental.

Because Dr. Fisher's views and beliefs undoubtedly have been influenced to some extent by unestimated thousands of books, papers, experiments, and discussions spanning more than half a century, it would be obviously impossible to acknowledge complete credits. And possibly it would be sheer ostentation in a book of this type, anyhow. But a word of sincere appreciation at this point would not be amiss, dedicated to all who have contributed in any measure to the growing stockpile of knowledge which may some day enable man to understand why he is what he is . . . and to consider seriously what, if anything, can be done about it.

LOWELL S. HAWLEY

# A Few Buttons Missing

# 1

*The training of children is a profession, where we must know how to lose time in order to gain it.*—ROUSSEAU

AFTER MORE THAN half a century of study and practice I have come to the sober conclusion that the life of a psychiatrist is not always a happy one. The typical patient enters your office dubious of his own sanity and departs some time later dubious of yours. Many of the people you meet classify you as a fraud and a charlatan while the others obviously consider you some sort of mystic mental healer flitting between the subconscious and the supernatural in a strange world of modern voodooism.

Mine is perhaps the most publicized and least understood branch of any profession in the world. Surely, if I had my life to live again guided by the knowledge I have acquired along the way, I should think twice before taking up the study of psychiatry. And after that, of course, I would trudge again in the same faltering footsteps, shouldering a smaller load of optimism at the start of the journey but retaining, I hope, the same eagerness; and attempting to acquire along the way a fuller measure of understanding.

To be truthful about it, I should concede that I did think twice before taking up the study of psychiatry. Only the first thought was provided by my father and the second one by my fiancée. I can neither take the credit nor shoulder the blame of being a self-made man.

My father, a hard-working God-fearing gentleman of the old school, somehow managed to acquire a modest fortune through the simple process of being in the right business at the right time. He owned a farm and cattle ranch in Illinois and built a packing house in Chicago. And when Prosperity smiled with a toothy grin, the family promptly moved to Boston and settled down in a fine old graystone mansion. Here my mother learned to soften her vowels and my father adapted himself beautifully to the dignity of his surroundings and contributed generously to the church.

For years the family lived as a Boston family should. My five older sisters and my two older brothers were educated in the traditional manner. But by the time I arrived on the scene in 1864, my father had reached that point in life where he thought a great deal about the good old days and about the way he had been raised, next to Nature and next to God—obviously the way a boy should be raised. And he startled my mother right out of her lorgnette by announcing that he was taking the baby of the family out West to be brought up in the saddle and to live the good life in the wide open spaces.

Since debate would have been futile and undignified, my mother shed a few quiet tears and sat back to bide her time. And I was hustled off to a four-section farm in Livingston County, Illinois, where my father gave me two saddle ponies and two collie dogs, and the task of herding 250 head of cattle from sunrise to sunset. For this service I received my board and room and ten cents a day in cash.

There were few fences on the prairie in those days. Human services were cheaper than barbed wire. And herds of cattle were tended much the same as flocks of sheep. Adjacent to my father's farm and separated only by an imaginary line were broad fields usually planted with corn and here I made my boyhood stand as gallantly as Horatio at the bridge. And the days of my boyhood were consumed in a ceaseless struggle to keep the cows out of the corn.

Since my father spent only a small portion of his time on the farm, my immediate human needs were tended largely by two Charlies. One was Chinaman Charlie, an ill-tempered curator of the kitchen who tended my diet and my laundry. And the other was Uncle Charlie, a bewhiskered and watery-eyed human fossil with a highly peppered personality and a mental age of six. As nearly as I ever learned, Uncle Charlie wasn't uncle to anybody. But he was called Uncle by everybody—probably to avoid confusion with Chinaman Charlie in the kitchen.

On Saturday nights, almost from the time I was eight years old, I was permitted to go along with the farmhands on their weekly excursions into the nearby town, where I generally watched the rig and guarded the newly purchased supplies while the boys made the most of their Saturday night off. But except for this weekly contact with society my boyhood resembled a slightly inverted version of the story of Heidi, the Goat Girl. Some of my best friends and my most bitter enemies were cattle. I learned to talk confidently to my ponies and they proved to be very good listeners. But my two inseparable companions were the two collie dogs—eager, honest, trustworthy, and responsive to my moods. Their shaggy hair absorbed practically all of my boyish tears. They consoled me in hours of loneliness and their joyous barking was an echo to youthful laughter. They had no capacity for resentment and no limit to devotion. And they admirably filled a basic need of childhood; to love and to be loved, without doubts or reservation.

It was my father's belief that a healthy mind is a natural by-product of a healthy body; that the world's most potent medicines are to be found in sunshine and clean fresh air and in the waters of a babbling brook, without any aid from an apothecary shop; and that the most important lessons in the world are learned without any aid from books.

"There'll be plenty of time for school and for books later on," he told my mother. "First he must build a strong body and a fine physique. Let him learn to hear the song of the wind and the rustle of leaves and all the music of the prairie, before you send him off to listen to some perspiring fiddle player in a stuffy hall."

When I was thirteen years old my mother quietly announced that the early experiment was ended. Nature could please arrange its commencement exercises, for little Jim was finished with his primary education in which the prairie took the place of a classroom.

When I returned to the family home I was, probably, the most freckle-faced and windburned and academically ignorant and, certainly, the most bowlegged boy in all of Boston. I had developed a

Midwestern drawl that greatly annoyed my mother's ears and I was a source of amazed amusement to the children of the neighborhood. They'd never seen a boy so big who could neither read nor write. And they stared in fascination.

However, by the time I was sixteen I had completely overtaken the boys of my age and had mastered in three years all the formal education they had acquired in eleven.

I was somewhat disillusioned in later years to discover that this was no particular proof of genius. Psychologists have demonstrated that a normal child commencing his academic education in adolescence can soon reach the same point of progress he would have achieved by starting to school at five or six years of age. I have often thought that if a child could be assured of a wholesome home life and proper physical development, this might provide the answer to a growing problem of inadequate classroom space and a shortage of qualified teachers—and the instinctive reluctance of all of us to hand over tax dollars for anything that doesn't fire bullets.

After graduation from public high school I entered the Massachusetts Institute of Technology for reasons more geographical than logical. It was just a few miles from home. But from the very start I was a square peg in a round hole. This might not have been so bad in itself if, in my youthful enthusiasm, I hadn't tried quite so hard to alter the hole to fit the peg. As gently as they could, faculty members explained to me that they had their own odd little notions of how their school should be run and if I didn't like it, why didn't I take my slipstick and my T-square and head for home? This I did, but it was a source of amazement to me for many years to come, to find M.I.T. still growing and still prospering without the benefit of my tuition or my advice.

I had no particular ambition at this point, that I can remember. And I believe I would have been perfectly content to remain at home and read books and attend occasional lawn parties. But once again it was the firm voice of my father that decided my immediate destiny.

"A young man needs to get out into the world and stand on his own two feet and prove what kind of stuff he's made of," he announced with conviction. And thus in the summer of 1885 I found myself driving a six-horse team along the dusty roads near Ventura, California, helping to haul a disgusting amount of lima beans to market. Hundred upon hundreds of acres of beans. Swarthy men with thick, Latin accents. A raw, red sun that burned down without mercy. And somehow an over-all shortage of time. Men worked on the double-quick. Foremen cursed and swore, and drivers backed their wagons to the loading platforms as if the fate of the world hung in the balance. One got the feeling that the nation would surely collapse from spontaneous malnutrition, if there should come an unscheduled two-minute delay in the frantic race to meet its insatiable appetite for lima beans.

It was gruelling, perspiration-soaked labor. But I learned to swear in Spanish and to sleep in my underwear, to chew tobacco and to spit to windward. I acquired a complexion like fine old leather; and a loathing for lima beans that has never diminished through the years.

And then I received a letter from my father who apparently had been backsliding on his Spartan philosophy for he told me that he'd arranged for me to take a job in the bank in San Diego. I collected my pay and headed south the following morning.

I had been only a few weeks in San Diego when I made a remarkable discovery: I could borrow ten thousand dollars from the bank on my signature alone. This was because I was young and sincere, had a reputation for honesty, and a good credit rating—plus the incidental fact that my father happened to be a major stockholder in the bank and would undoubtedly pay back the money if I should default.

So I took the ten thousand dollars and embarked upon a fascinating game of Monopoly, long before it had ever become established as a parlor pastime. San Diego was a sleepy little metropolis where tired old men spoke boastfully of the climate and where eager youngsters listened to the lure of the larger cities, far away. There was money in San Diego, but mostly it was retirement money. It belonged to old men who had come there to die; and my distinction rested largely in being a young man who had come there to live.

In a plot hastily sketched over a mid-morning cup of coffee, I started out quietly to buy up options on San Diego real estate. The market was static and the options were easy to secure. And then at the psychological moment I made an outright purchase of a hillside lot for two hundred dollars, cash. This was significant enough to cause comment around town . . . but not nearly so much comment as occurred several weeks later when I sold the same lot to a man named Arthur Nason, for five hundred dollars. I'd made three hundred dollars profit in a matter of a few weeks, and I was gazed upon with new respect about town. But that wasn't the end of it. Several weeks later I bought back the lot for an "unidentified client," paying Mr. Nason eight hundred dollars.

Before it was over, real estate prices in the area were skyrocketing. Speculators were moving in cautiously. And pinpointed through the area were the lots on which I held options. Arthur Nason and I had tossed the same lot back and forth until we had the price up well over a thousand dollars, and the County Recorder could practically recite the legal description of the property from memory, he'd filed it so many times.

By now the original subterfuge was plainly apparent, and we operated openly as Fisher & Nason. But by now it didn't matter. The boom was on, and far too fascinating for anyone to withdraw.

One of my close friends was an unusually astute young man about town named John D. Spreckels who rode the boom with an almost fanatical faith in the future of San Diego. And emboldened by his optimism I continued buying options on downtown real estate and holding them just long enough to collect a substantial profit.

The god that is supposed to watch over fools must have been in a benevolent mood, for at the end of two and a half years I had amassed more than a hundred thousand dollars. I had built and at that time I owned the Albermarle Hotel in downtown San Diego. In a moment of disgust I had bought a rickety old wagon and a tired old horse, and hired a Negro to haul baggage from the depot for the benefit of hotel guests and other interested parties. And I had watched this modest enterprise grow into the San Diego and Coronado Transfer Company of which I was President; boasting dozens of up-to-the-minute highly varnished wagons brought in from Illinois. And in addition to the horses needed here, I owned and operated one of the better livery stables.

In association with a colorful character about town, "White Hat" McCarthy, I had been importing five-gaited horses from Kentucky and selling them at a fabulous profit in the midst of the spiraling boom. And on a wild hunch I had bought sixty acres up the coast at Oceanside, marked it off in thirty and fifty foot lots and started one of the first California subdivisions.

It was all so fantastically easy that I couldn't imagine why everyone in the country couldn't be independently wealthy. It was my first real business experience and I am afraid that I never realized there was any risk involved. Neither did it occur to me to mention to my father that he was a moral co-signer on my note at the bank. Those were the days when money yielding a six or eight percent return was considered idle money, and my various scattered investments were commencing to compound themselves in startling fashion. But at that point I had the misfortune of becoming homesick. I dreamed of walking along the streets of Boston, not as a boy but as a man who had already made his place in the world. And when the dreams became irresistible I sold out and headed for home. I had struggled in the world of business for two and a half years, hadn't I? Now I was ready to retire.

My father, for some inexplicable reason, seemed deeply concerned about the ten thousand dollars I had borrowed from the bank. He did not seem particularly impressed by what I had done with it. But in the end he gave me some fatherly advice about safe, conservative, Boston-style investments which would yield modest and dependable interest.

It is not easy, however, for a speculator to become an investor. Father was old. He had probably grown deaf to the loud knockings of Opportunity. I did my best to explain to him that times had changed, and that the world of 1888 was a modern, fast-moving world. But he seemed unconvinced.

By now I guess the god of fools had become a bit impatient with me, and was maybe tired of smiling. I lost money faster in staid old

Boston with its quiet air, than I had ever acquired it in the brawling, booming city of San Diego.

My father, in the ensuing years, became deeply concerned about the future stewardship of the rather extensive enterprise he had built up through so many years of struggle. Mrs. O'Leary's cow had knocked many of the props from under his Chicago packing business and subtle changes were commencing to appear on the prairie. Fences were being strung and labor costs were mounting. Expanding railroad facilities were bringing distant competition to the cattle business. Capital and sweat were no longer the two chief ingredients of success in that field, and it was becoming increasingly obvious that scientific knowledge and careful management would be required for survival.

These things my father explained to me, and then offered to make me an outright gift of the cattle ranch where I had lived as a boy, upon the condition that I should first take a degree at Harvard in Veterinary Medicine. It was a tantalizing prize to dangle before the eyes of a disillusioned and slightly bewildered young man who had no great inward surge of ambition, and I am sure neither my father nor I ever questioned the ethics or the wisdom of such occupational bribery. I had lost all interest in the world of business and the field of speculation, and while I was never completely thrilled with the idea of becoming a bovine midwife, I quietly followed the path of least resistance.

Among my graduating gifts when I had completed my study at Harvard was a black broad-brimmed hat which I wore proudly through the streets of Boston and placed at the feet of a beautiful young lady who was so prominent in the social register that she spoke with equal familiarity to the Cabots, to the Lowells, and to God. But when she spoke to me that day she made it quite emphatic that she would never marry a horse doctor.

Upon cross-examination I discovered that she might look upon such a union more favorably if I held a degree of M.D. instead of M.D.V. And since all the credits of my first two years would apply toward a medical degree, I placed the broad-brimmed hat far back in the closet and started off once again to Harvard.

I never felt that my father was completely happy about my sudden decision to forsake the important field of veterinary medicine to go probing into the needs and the whims of the human species. He blamed himself somewhat for having used undue influence in forcing the selection of my original college studies. But I never felt that this early training was entirely wasted.

No man who has lived with cows on the prairie and who has studied them in the laboratory can fail to ask himself the inevitable question: Why aren't there more contented *people?* And that question, in my opinion, is the very crux of the whole involved problem of mental and physical health.

And then there was one other thing: After you have neatly and efficiently blown a pill down a horse's throat you can not readily re-adjust to the demands of routine medical practice. I realized that I could never sit quietly at the bedside of some wealthy Boston dowager and watch her choke and gag on pills slightly larger than mustard seeds. There would be the ever-present temptation to grab up a glass tube from the medicine tray and make like an African native with a blow-gun. It seemed advisable from the outset to seek some branch of medicine not dependent upon the administration of pills. And since I had no inclination toward surgery, the study of psychiatry loomed as the logical answer.

Upon graduation I served my internship in the Boston Children's Hospital and soon thereafter left for a year of study in Vienna. I met Sigmund Freud and explored the strange avenues he had pioneered. And I met other men who had also met Sigmund Freud and who dis-agreed with his theories violently. I gathered a strange assortment of truths and untruths. And I learned, ironically, that some of the untruths had come from the laboratory, while some of the truths had been handed down by the medicine men of an earlier, savage era. I studied psychiatry through a turbulent, hectic period—where the task each morning was to forget three-fourths of what had been learned the day before and had subsequently been disproved; and where the task each night was to remember half of what had been purposely forgotten in the morning because the theories which disproved these things had been themselves disproved.

After a year of intensive study in this threshing-machine atmosphere I again returned to Boston, but the ensuing three years saw me off to Zurich, to Paris, and to Leipzig. And then with the grim prospect of my fortieth birthday dead ahead, I solemnly decided it was high time to put my accumulated knowledge to work. I felt I had progressed to to the point where I could separate the wheat from the chaff, and I returned from Europe with a burning zeal to rectify all that was wrong with humanity and to carry the bright light of reason into the dark recesses of ignorance and folly.

By this time the young lady who had once refused to marry a horse doctor was married to a fine young chap who was not a horse doctor, and so far as I know they lived happily ever after. To prove there was no resentment on my part I soon married a young lady with whom I had been corresponding for a number of years, and we left immediately for the west coast where I established a general medical practice, setting bones and delivering babies. This was 1904 and Los Angeles appealed to us as the coming metropolis, even though it didn't offer any demands for a full-time psychiatrist. Among other duties in the ensuing years, I assumed a position as Superintendent of the Los Angeles Psychopathic Hospital which was at that time the second largest in the United States, and I also accepted a professorship and served as assistant Dean of the small medical college that was later to become the medical school of the University of Southern California.

In addition I have made nineteen trips to Europe to further my study of psychiatry. In World War I, I served as psychiatrist in a base hospital in Alsace-Lorraine. In World War II, I served as psychiatric examiner of the boys between nineteen and twenty-eight years of age at the induction center in Los Angeles. In 1946, being by now a strapping youngster eighty-two years of age, I left my home to spend a year in a hospital in Peru, studying the new therapy of psychosomatic medicine. In somewhat more than a half century of practice, I have examined unestimated thousands of normal and abnormal persons.

I have read and studied thousands of books, pamphlets, and papers
upon nearly every phase of the entire psychiatric field. But never since
that early trip home from Europe have I had a great deal of confidence in my wheat-and-chaff separating ability.

Psychiatrists today are not unlike the cartographers of five hundred
years ago, attempting to draw maps of vast areas yet unexplored—
depending upon a small amount of knowledge diluted with theory,
rumor, and intuition. It is sometimes difficult to know where actual
knowledge ends and unproven theory begins. And yet this is the way
of progress. You can't wait until all the world is explored before the
first map is drawn, else the more extensive exploration could never be
achieved.

In the review of facts and theories there is much difference of
opinion among today's psychiatrists. This is perhaps understandable
when one considers that members of the United States Supreme Court,
interpreting the same laws, arrive at exactly opposing opinions, after
hearing the same arguments and reviewing the same evidence at the
same time in the same courtroom. Psychiatrists, on the other hand,
must study a much wider variety of conflicting evidence. No two of
them ever hear exactly the same arguments all the way through. And
what they do hear, they must attempt to interpret in relation to laws
that haven't yet been discovered.

The charge has been made that psychiatry does not fit the pattern
of a true science, but is composed of a strange hodgepodge of psychology, pathology, philosophy, anthropology, and man's insatiable
desire to hear himself talk.

Certainly the original Freudian approach toward psychoanalysis was
not entirely scientific, in an impartial laboratory sense. Psychiatry, by
its very nature, must pursue the will-o'-the-wisp of irrational human
thought wherever it may choose to stray. And who is to draw the
precise boundary lines of such a far-flung pursuit and glibly decide
when the psychiatrist is out of bounds?

The study of psychiatry is the study of man; of his environment
and his heredity, and of all factors which affect these things. It does
not neatly fit into an isolated groove.

Still, in my opinion, much of the bewildered confusion which surrounds this comparatively new branch of medical science springs from the preconviction that it is complex, mysterious, and practically impossible for the average man to understand.

If and when we do more fully understand it; if and when we have separated the wheat from the chaff, then, in my firm conviction, we will find its basic truths to be simple, logical, and entirely reasonable—as are all other basic truths on this earth.

# 2

*We go by the major vote, and if the majority are insane, the sane must go to the hospital.*—H. MANN

AMONG MY CLOSE friends of many years has been an elderly sportsman who grew up in the furniture business and who inherited a profitable and well-established retail furniture firm from his father.

One afternoon when we were out fishing, drifting idly across the still waters of a mountain lake, he became thoughtfully talkative about his particular mission in life.

"You know, I figure I'm a pretty lucky guy to be in the furniture business," he mused. "Mostly when folks come into my store, they're happy. Maybe they're young couples just setting up housekeeping. Or they're older folks, who've finally saved enough money to buy something they've wanted for years. Or if they don't buy, they're busy wishing. You can see their dreams written all over them.

"And I've thought to myself: What would it have been like if my father had been an undertaker, and I'd inherited a mortuary? What would it be like if the people you see every day were sad, and you looked into eyes filled with tears instead of eyes that are filled with dreams?"

He practically shuddered as he talked about it, and I couldn't keep from smiling. "You'd get used to it," I assured him glibly. "Lots of fine people are undertakers. And besides, if you didn't like it you could sell out and go into something you liked better." But he merely shook his head.

"I'm not the type, Jim. I'd just keep plodding along the way I started. I wouldn't realize there was any better way of life. And eventually, I guess, I'd just shrivel up and die with so much sadness around me all the time. I need happiness around me, the way an alcoholic needs his bottle. Take that away and life wouldn't be worth living."

He eyed me thoughtfully for a moment and continued, "Even worse than being an undertaker, I'd imagine, must be this business of being a psychiatrist. People don't come to see you unless there's something wrong with them. Every case is a tragedy of some kind, right off the bat. Every patient has at least a few buttons missing. Sometimes I wonder how you can stand it, without going a little bit wacky yourself?"

And the odd part of it all was the fact that until that afternoon I'd often felt sorry for him. It must seem like a futile sort of life, I'd told myself, merely buying and selling a bunch of furniture and having no greater goal in life than to pile up a few more dollars at the end of each month. How could it possibly be interesting, if you didn't particularly need the dollars in the first place?

But I sat that evening beside a campfire and tried to imagine what my life would have been like if I'd remained as a real estate speculator in San Diego, or if I'd followed through with my plans to be a bovine midwife on a farm in Illinois. I tried to picture myself as an engineer who'd graduated with honors from M.I.T., busy building great bridges and highways for the commerce of a nation. But all the little pictures seemed drab and uninspiring. And reviewing my life from the twilight shadows, it seemed that every incident from my earliest recollection had been woven into my life with but a single purpose. A thousand little experiences from my boyhood apparently would have been without significance to a jeweler, a real estate speculator, a veterinary, or an engineer. For even though I didn't realize it at the time, they were primary lessons for a potential psychiatrist.

The moving finger having writ, moved on. But I secretly suspected that it must have had the entire plot in mind from the outset.

Looking back, I could see how my daily duties on the farm constituted a sneak-preview of my later mission in life.

With my pony and my two collie dogs, it was my task to drive the cattle out to the higher pastureland which lay toward the back of the farm. And while an attempt was made to keep the herd moving to new grazing areas day by day, still the drive followed the same general course to start with—out the long lane past the orchard, down across the swale where a small stream meandered, and then up again to the higher ground beyond.

This was a clearly defined trail that followed the natural contour of the ground and it had become deeply worn through years of usage. It wasn't the shortest route to the back pasture, nor was it necessarily the best route. It was merely the established route, and there seemed no logical reason to change it.

Through long habit, most of the cattle followed the trail quite obediently and they moved along as a docile herd. But there were always a few ornery critters defying all regimentation. They'd veer off sharply to the right or left after coming out of the lane. With wild shouts and frantic yappings, we'd head them off and turn them back again into the herd.

And looking back, it seems to me that my mission in life has changed very little after establishing myself as a psychiatrist. For here, too, my task has been one of pursuing the strays and attempting to drive them back into the human herd.

For the sake of efficiency in operating a complex world, as in operating a cattle ranch, it is necessary to keep the herd together. It is necessary to follow the established trail. And it is necessary, apparently, to have psychiatrists, like well-trained cow dogs, to heckle and bedevil the strays and to prevent an occasional wayfarer from falling into the silo.

The average man's course through life traces a meandering and highly peculiar pattern, which tradition has recognized as the norm. And because it is the established route we must accept it as being the correct route.

We have no way of knowing what man is supposed to be like or how he is supposed to behave. We can merely judge him by how he is. We can do little more than accept the premise: As he is, so should he be.

The point of demarcation between normality and abnormality is purely an imaginary line sketched for the sake of convenience. As a youngster I had to reckon with the fact that a herd tightly bunched could not properly graze. I had to realize that there could be leaders and stragglers widely separated. And I had to learn to distinguish between those cattle forming the outer fringes of a fanned-out herd, and those deliberate strays heading off toward the corn fields. It was strangely similar to the eternal problems confronting the psychiatrist.

All of us, unfortunately, are "queer" to a certain extent. Only some more so than others. When the abnormality is modest, the individual is generously considered normal. When it is extreme, he is considered abnormal. But there remains a fuzzy no-man's-land in between, where a decision either way could be open to honest question. And it is here in this no-man's-land that the psychiatrist must do much of his work. Here will be found the transient cases or the incipient psychoses, the bulk of the neurotics—the casual strays still capable of being driven back toward the norm.

On the farm, particularly, I remember old Maud—a wild-eyed cow who wore one crumpled horn at a rakish angle over her forehead and whose unconquered spirit waged eternal war with the two collies. They'd nip at her heels and bark at her head. And old Maud would either bow her neck and charge or she'd kick out ungracefully with a hind foot. And on rare occasions she'd send one of the dogs sprawling and yelping.

Old Maud was a rugged individualist. Even before we got out of the lane in the morning she'd plant herself wrong way of the herd and commence nudging the flanks of other cattle filing past. Just plain ornery. At the creek she'd wade out to mid-stream and drink; and then stand there with the water dripping from her mouth while she surveyed the landscape in all directions, like a quarterback looking over the field before calling the next play. Then she'd be off again with two collies and a small boy trying desperately to head her off.

At first I used to get so infuriated with her that I'd come back to the farmhouse with tears streaming down my cheeks, and sometimes I'd have nightmares. But it was Uncle Charlie who taught me how to be philosophical about such things.

"Some day you're a-gonna grow up to be a big man, and maybe your pa will let you be the boss of this whole bloomin' ranch," he told me. "But now you take old Maud, she ain't never goin' to be nothin' but a cow. She got nothin' to look forward to, 'cept some day bein' driv' to the slaughter house. When she acts ornery that-a-way, why it's jest her idea of havin' fun. It's the only kind of fun she knows how to have."

I'd never looked at it quite that way. And I tried, after that, to be a bit more tolerant of old Maud. At times it seemed to help. But I couldn't explain this viewpoint to my two dogs. And they were even bitterer toward old Maud than I had ever been.

Then, too, it was easy to be philosophical about it in the evening sitting around the farmhouse. It wasn't quite so easy in the daytime out on the prairie when old Maud was making life miserable at the moment. And so I pleaded with Mr. Burton, the ranch foreman, to try to get rid of her next time he had to thin the herd.

Shortly after that old Maud was singled out for the long trek to the slaughter house, and I made the mistake of stopping by the small corral to take one last look at her. I imagined I could see a look of reproach in her big soulful eyes. And I knew, all of a sudden, how Judas must have felt. For weeks those eyes haunted me. Out on the prairie I could imagine her up in Cow Heaven, looking down upon me with resentment. And I earnestly beseeched God to please explain to her that I hadn't really meant anything personal by it, and that I begged her forgiveness.

And all of this, it seemed in retrospect, must have been but an elaborate dress rehearsal for a performance yet to come.

From my professional practice, I particularly remember Alice O., a psychopathic version of old Maud in human form—an unpredictable youthful delinquent who'd spent most of her nineteen years in breaking away from the human herd and making life miserable for those who had attempted to keep her on the clearly defined trail of social acceptability.

From a professional standpoint, her case might not be considered particularly interesting nor in any way unusual. But to me it was entirely unforgettable. She was the first person ever to be deprived of freedom as a result of my professional testimony. And for months the memory of her eyes haunted me, just as had the eyes of old Maud many years before. And once again I pleaded with God to please act as intermediary and to make her somehow understand that I had merely done my duty as I had seen it.

It is ironically unfortunate, I believe, when a young psychiatrist must render his first court-requested opinion in the judgment of a psychopathic personality. There are many other mental disorders that are quite clear and sharp, and more easily defined. You can readily assure yourself that the schizophrenic or the paranoid individual is being confined for his own ultimate good. But there is plenty of reason to suspect that the individual with a psychopathic personality is being put away for the convenience of society as a whole . . . to make life easier for those who must tend the herd.

It is reasonably easy, I discovered later, to maintain an impersonal and impartial attitude toward the advanced schizophrenic who sits like a lump of human clay, unmoved and unmoving.

But Alice O. wasn't like that. She was attractive, in a disheveled sort of way. Her eyes were bright and clear and comprehending. She answered questions with ready coöperation and her intelligence seemed well above average She smiled readily, and she confided to me, almost whimsically, that she guessed this time she'd gotten into more trouble than she'd bargained for.

She was the youngest of three children from a respectable family. There was no official record of mental abnormality in the family, although it developed that a maternal aunt had been "sent away" to some kind of private rest home years before and the family refused to discuss it.

Alice, as a child, had demonstrated frequent temper tantrums and at an early age had exhibited extreme jealousy of her older brother and sister when they were given privileges not granted Alice because of her younger age. The older brother and sister appeared perfectly normal and had good scholastic records.

Alice, on the other hand, had been transferred from one school to another because of her inability to get along well with either teachers or students. She had twice been sent to private boarding schools, but had run away on both occasions.

She admitted frequent and indiscriminate sexual relationships since the age of fourteen, including a pregnancy and an abortion when she was sixteen, and venereal infection the year before. She insisted that she derived no satisfaction from these relationships, and she guessed she did it "just to have something to do."

Two months before being picked up by the police, she had left home and had stayed most of that time with a man twenty-five years her senior. He was a married man whose family was touring Europe, and the resulting scandal had provided a tabloid field day.

There had been strange goings on at the big house with the drawn blinds during the past two months, it developed, and usually with Alice as the center of attraction. And the affair had come to the attention of police after she had fired three revolver shots at her host during the course of a nocturnal quarrel.

"I'm awfully sorry about that part of it," she told me seriously, "but he called me names that no nice girl would stand for. When I went and got the gun out of his bureau drawer he just laughed and dared me to shoot him." She shrugged her shoulders and smiled wryly. "If he didn't want me to shoot him he shouldn't have dared me to do it. And he shouldn't have called me names."

Under questioning, she insisted that she could see nothing wrong with her behavior, except for the episode with the gun. It was her life, and her body, and why couldn't people mind their own business?

Asked about the reported wild parties that had been going on for two months, she quietly pointed out that nobody had to come to the parties if they didn't want to. "And if they came and if they had fun, what business is it of anybody else's?"

When I asked her if she believed her behavior had been entirely normal she replied hotly: "How other people behave is their business. You'll have to ask them about that. How I behave is my business and I wish people would leave me alone!"

Explaining that it was more or less a hypothetical question, I asked her if she would rather be sent to the hospital for observation right away, or if she'd prefer to wait for some time and face the possibility of a confinement that might last for several years. At first she insisted that she could see no reason why a hospital should even be mentioned, "If they want to put me in jail for the shooting, that's all right with me. I probably have it coming. But there's no earthly reason to talk about hospitals and observations. I'm not crazy, Doctor, any more than you are."

When I insisted upon an answer to my question she thought it over for a moment and then announced triumphantly:

"If I could have a choice, I'd rather wait and take a chance of spending several years in confinement later on. Inside of six months, who knows? I may be dead, anyhow."

It was a leading question, as were several others I asked. But her answers, all the way through, were reasonably typical of the psychopathic personality: Take the easiest way out at the moment, and let tomorrow take care of itself. And this, coupled with the demonstrated childish attitude toward the taking of a dare and the rather incongruous resentment toward being called a name which no "nice" girl would tolerate, offered significant evidence of abnormality in view of the long history of unorthodox behavior.

In this particular case I had but one responsibility: To report back to the court whether, in my professional opinion, the girl was mentally normal. My diagnosis was that of a psychopathic personality, and with that opinion vanished all hopes for probation. Since my responsibility had ended, there was no reason to go exploring through the records of the past, or to attempt to track down all accessories before the fact, and all incidents that had contributed to the delinquency of a minor. My job was ended. But for weeks I was haunted by the memory of those petulant and somehow reproachful eyes, gazing at me from across the courtroom table.

They were the eyes of a hurt child. Physically and mentally, Alice had become a big girl. Emotionally, she was still a child in pigtails . . . a very spoiled and a very confused little girl wrapped up inside a big and shapely and thumb-worn package.

To speak of her as mentally ill is hardly appropriate. Surely she was as completely sane as any person in the courtroom. But like old Maud, she was intent upon having the only kind of fun she knew how to have, regardless of any inconvenience to others. She had refused to follow the established trail, and something had to be done about it.

# 3

*I am a part of all that I have met.*—TENNYSON

AMONG THE MEN who most greatly influenced the course of my medical career was our old but dramatic family physician, Dr. Joseph Beason. During my later years at Harvard, and more particularly during the time of my internship at Boston Children's Hospital, I developed a strong affection toward him. Often when I could get away I would stop by his office and we'd sit in the back room discussing the weighty problems of the world while he brewed a pot of evil-tasting tea over a gas jet and continually refilled my cup. His heart-warming and tongue-scorching hospitality was equally matched by his eloquence.

He was a tall, gaunt man who invariably reminded me of Abraham Lincoln, and he spoke of such noble things as Man's Gallant Conquest of Disease.

"You will live to see the greatest victories in this long struggle," he used to tell me. "Within the span of your lifetime you will see the Flaming Sword of Knowledge strike down the ruthless enemies of this mortal life, and man at last will stand triumphant over his ancient enemy, Disease."

It sounded exciting, the way he told it. And just a little bloodthirsty. He'd clasp his long arms behind his back between sessions with the makeshift teapot, and stalk back and forth across the room, delivering flowery orations in a strangely impressive monotone.

"My years of service are drawing toward a close," he'd announce flatly. "I will never be on hand for the great victory parade. But you, my boy, will live to hear the joyous shouting of the multitude, and

32

you will march as one of the conquering heroes of this holy crusade. And when at last it comes time to drink the victory toast, just save one passing thought for old Dr. Beason who'll be there with you in spirit."

Under different circumstances he possibly could have been the world's most proficient recruiting sergeant. As it was, he was just a tired old man with a wonderful dream; a doctor of medicine but a student of philosophy. For twenty-five years he had religiously attended his patients and neglected his accounts in the industrial environs of New York and had returned to Boston to enjoy the remnants of a dwindling family fortune. He was a man of social prominence and professional obscurity. But he inspired me with visions of the better world of tomorrow, and he sent me back to the hospital each day feeling a little like Sir Lancelot in quest of the Holy Grail.

With vaccines and greater sanitation, with increasing literacy throughout the nation and greater public interest in matters of health, I too commenced to envision the day when there'd be little need for hospitals and clinics as we knew them then, and when medical science could devote itself largely to preventive measures.

It was largely through Dr. Beason's influence that I took extra training in the maternity ward, cautiously believing that this one branch of medical service, alone, might never be completely outmoded, and that the Flaming Sword would observe its respectful limitations.

As a family physician, Dr. Beason wasn't the most desirable practitioner in the world, for he spent a large share of his time addressing public gatherings wherever they could be found—men's business clubs, women's study clubs, Bible classes, and sailors' missions, or any other groups that would consent to listen. His routine medical calls weren't permitted to interfere with his lecture work. And the gavel, to him, had become more important than the mortar or the scalpel.

"Worthwhile progress isn't made by sitting at the bedside of a single individual," he used to tell me. "That's like sitting and poking one finger into a hole in the dike, rather than striking out against the cause of the problem itself. 'There are thousands hacking at the branches of evil, to one who is striking at the root.'"

It was his firm belief that in widespread public education lay the only real hope of progress and eventual victory.

"You can't win the great battle against Pestilence by leaving all the fighting to the professional medical men, like hired Hessian soldiers," he used to shout from the platform. "What we need is a vast citizen's army, like those immortal Minute Men of long ago. Let every home be a bastion in the fight against Disease. Let every intelligent adult be a volunteer in the great crusade, spreading knowledge of the simple rules of health. And then, my friends, we shall strike down and destroy man's ancient and ruthless enemies, Ignorance and Disease!"

He was entirely earnest and strangely impressive. And I imagine he influenced me far more than I realized at the time. For I have carried, always, a sense of ultimate futility when applying myself to the retail end of the business, concerned solely with the care and treatment of single individuals . . . too preoccupied with the work at hand to give much thought to the prevention of similar maladies that may affect others walking unwarned along the same hazardous pathway toward the same pitfalls.

I have never been entirely satisfied to consider myself as a modern version of the little Dutch boy at the dike. At one time in my life I crusaded vehemently for the sterilization of mental misfits prior to their release from state-operated institutions, and I had the satisfaction of seeing such a program adopted in many states, following the lead of Indiana in 1907—until today such a program is in effect to greater or lesser extent in twenty-six states. Like Dr. Beason I have perhaps responded almost too readily to the call of the lecture platform, and I've responded also to the call of the classroom. I have wallowed through the mire of politics in seeking intelligent legislative action in regard to sexual abnormals. I've lived to see the futility of many inspired dreams. And I've lived through psychiatry's era of trial and error—contributing, I'd imagine, my fair share to both.

I have faced the unspoken but obvious rebuke of many contemporaries who believe that the physician should remain in his clinic and content himself with the responsibility of combating human ills upon a one-at-a-time basis. And I have lived long enough to realize that they are perhaps more nearly correct than I once would have admitted.

And yet I hold nothing but profound respect for the long-departed Dr. Beason, and for his cherished dream. I have been waiting faithfully for more than half a century, firmly resolved to drink a toast to his memory at the great victory banquet. I have never forgotten the promise made long ago.

But there is no banquet. And no victory parade. I have heard no joyous shouting of the multitude. And the Flaming Sword of Knowledge apparently has swung back to slice a host of volunteer crusaders.

There's no doubt that tremendous advances have been made by the medical profession since Dr. Beason paraded back and forth across his office and gave eloquent voice to his vision of things-to-come. We've developed new wonder drugs. The public has gained vast new knowledge of vitamins, nutrition, and basic habits of health. Medical efficiency has improved and finer facilities are available.

And on at least one point Dr. Beason was correct: Many of the diseases that demanded so much of a physician's time in his day have now been largely eradicated.

Typhoid fever, smallpox, diarrhea and enteritis in infants, pneumonia, and many other maladies that kept physicians frantically busy fifty years ago, today occupy a proportionately smaller amount of the typical physician's time.

And yet his waiting room is today more crowded than ever. Hospital rooms can't be built fast enough to meet the demand. The multitudes clamoring for relief continue to increase. The mentally ill multiply in number. And the modern medical man is not unlike the modern housewife who's so frantically busy operating all her various labor-saving devices that she barely has time to eat.

Both the medical man and the housewife suffer from the development of a hypercritical attitude. Fifty years ago a small amount of dust in the parlor and a few aches and pains scattered about the anatomy were generally to be expected, and were usually overlooked. Today both are gazed upon with horror and regarded as abnormal.

Grandpa used to take a couple of minutes out from his cultivating, wipe his forehead on his shirtsleeve, and explain to the hired man: "I've got me a bellyache. Sumpin' I et, no doubt." And two minutes later he'd be back at work.

The modern man is more apt to try his hand at self-diagnosis, attempting to trace each twinge of pain across his abdomen, while weighing the symptoms as an indication of acute appendicitis or abdominal cancer.

The benefits of increased education are difficult to see at this point. As man has acquired a great amount of leisure and a small amount of knowledge, he has found time to focus more and more attention upon the most fascinating character of his world: Himself.

In his role as an amateur and highly enthusiastic diagnostician, he searches eagerly for any signs of abnormality—physical, mental, or emotional. Through such introspection he may discover for the first time a number of more or less normal bodily functions. And because he hadn't been aware of them in the past, he is apt to consider them abnormal.

A classic example was the man who came to me with strong but apparently unfounded convictions of hopeless homosexual tendencies. And not until after several visits did he blurt out the horrifying story of his chance discovery:

"Doctor, I'm going to tell you something. You've probably noticed that my breasts are large, almost like a woman's? Well, there's something else that's very odd. If I rub my breasts the nipples pop out, just like a woman's!"

"Mr. X," I replied, "I'm going to tell you something. I have noticed that your breasts are large. So are your jowls. So is your abdomen. You could afford to lose nearly twenty pounds through an intelligent program of exercise and diet. And you may be interested to know that any normal man can rub his breasts and cause the nipples to pop out, as you say. It's a peculiarity of the species."

And yet that simple chance discovery of a normal bodily function, combined with a fading potency and a dwindling interest in his equally obese wife, plus a great amount of time spent in introspection, had all but convinced him that he was homosexual. There were several other complications in his particular case. But his basic trouble, all in all, was the result of spending not enough time on the road and spending too much time in the shower—having too little interest in others, and too much interest in himself.

In order to truly understand himself, a man must also understand his fellow men. He must understand the world in which he lives, and his relationship to that world. It is impossible for him to tell whether or not he is out of step with those around him, by gazing at his own feet alone.

For a modest investment of money and a still more modest investment of time, the layman can skip-read through the super-dehydrated concentration of an abbreviated article in a vest-pocket magazine and gain a hazy notion about such things as the super-ego and the inferiority complex. By checking his answers to a set of twenty questions, he can decide whether he's an introvert or an extrovert; typically masculine or typically feminine; and whether he has the soul of an artist or all the aesthetic temperament of a bull elephant.

From the furtive view under half-closed eyelids, he may gallantly attempt to psychoanalyze his friends and neighbors as well as himself, modestly believing that he can achieve in twenty-five minutes what a trained psychoanalyst could hardly hope to achieve in less than many months or years.

But it is not, unfortunately, an entirely harmless pastime. And psychoanalysis was never designed as a spectator sport.

In the fertile fields of his own apprehensive and misguided imagination, he may develop one sweet bunch of neuroses and find himself deeply lacerated by the imaginary thorns.

Man's ability to learn mathematics, history, and grammar, has never surpassed his ability to learn new and more dramatic ways of suffering, once he's really put his mind to it.

Acute pains in conjunction with menstruation, for example, are fairly common in the Western world, and among the more educated women in the Orient. But they are seldom found among women from the uneducated and stoical masses who have never been the subjects of any great amounts of enlightenment, sentiment, or sympathy. Primitive women of South Africa were found free from complaints by Dr. A. S. Heyns who made an intensive study of the subject. Dr. M. C. Aaberg, who made his studies among the primitive women of Guam, found that nausea and vomiting during pregnancy and the more acute pains of childbirth were rare, or totally unknown, prior to the native's contact with culture.

But the native lassie learns to experience the aches and pains of the Western world, almost before she learns to chew its gum or wear its shoes. And sedatives follow closely in the wake of that departed ignorance which was bliss.

If knowledge, in itself, were sufficient to guarantee a long and happy and healthy life, then surely our physicians and surgeons would be among the more long-lived of the population, for their knowledge on health matters is supposedly great. A healthy mind and a healthy body are the results of what the individual is born with and how he lives; they are not the result of how much he knows. And on that point I'm afraid Dr. Beason would have to bow to the nonprofessional ideas of my father. Education can be but a partial answer, at best.

It has been conclusively proved that our taste preferences are acquired. It is reasonable to assume that those preferences will in some measure determine the individual's daily diet—and his diet will directly affect the physical development of his body.

Emotions, as we shall see, affect the digestive process and this in turn determines what part of the body's fuel intake is to be put to proper use. Emotions also affect the use or the abuse of various organs of the body.

The social environment in which we live obviously affects the emotions. The aforementioned taste preferences are but a small part of the preference-prejudice pattern set up through experience, observation, and imitation. Even though his mother can't bake all the ice crystals out of a frozen pie, the child grows up with the conviction that she is the best cook in all the world, and the finest foods are exactly like the ones that mother used to thaw.

The climate in which we live is a definite factor in influencing bodily functions, food intake, metabolism, and so on. It determines in some measure our habits and our hobbies and our interests . . . and our attitudes.

Psychological tests have demonstrated that even the color of wallpaper in a room may affect body efficiency and emotional behavior. Styles of dress and types of shoes may confine the body and affect the posture, and leave their indelible stamp upon the state of mind and the breadth of the horizon. Who wants to cultivate new hobbies or pursue new interests when his feet are killing him?

From these myriad influences emerges the man as he is. And he expects a ready and concise answer when he demands: "In simple words, Doc, tell me why I feel the way I do."

But even more disconcerting, of course, is the patient who announces in effect: "Just sit back and listen, Doc, and I'll explain to *you* exactly what's the cause of my trouble."

Such a man was Mr. C., a prominent but B-grade movie actor who was induced to seek psychiatric help several years ago after two unsuccessful attempts at suicide. Because of the nature of the attempts and the nature of the failures, there were reasons to suspect that the efforts had been only half-hearted, at best, and I came to suspect later that they had been mere dramatizations.

"You wouldn't think, to look at me, that I'd be the type to lose interest in living," he announced at the very outset of the first interview. "People probably look at me and think: There's a man who has everything. Money. Women. Prestige. Fame, in a certain sort of way. Not bad-looking. Everything that a man could wish for."

He paused dramatically, but when I offered no comment he continued. "Money doesn't hold any interest for me any more. I have a nice home with a swimming pool, all paid for. I own two cars, both Cadillacs. I could buy more if I wanted them, but why? I owned a beautiful cruiser down at Balboa but I sold it a couple months ago . . . not because I needed the money, but because I'd lost all interest in the boat."

He leaned forward and looked directly into my eyes from across the desk and explained in a dramatic whisper, "Doctor, I have everything that a man could wish for . . . except the ability to wish for things!" He explained how, before he'd come to Hollywood, he used to skimp and save to get the money to buy a new suit of clothes. "It was fun, Doctor. I'd wear my new suit to a dance, and get a big charge out of it. Now I go down and order three or four suits at a time, but it isn't any fun. By the time they're delivered, I've almost forgotten that I ordered them."

"You seem to have about the same kind of trouble that bothered old King Midas," I suggested, and he nodded his head in solemn agreement. "That's about the size of it, I'm afraid."

"Or an Alexander, with no more worlds to conquer?"

He commenced to nod again, then eyed me sharply. "My trouble, Doctor, is that I've done everything I ever wanted to do. I'm really a simple sort of person at heart. My wants are simple, and they've all been more than satisfied. And—well—life has lost its sparkle. I've reached the point where I just don't give a damn about anything."

"Have you ever discussed this with anyone else?" I asked. And once again he eyed me almost suspiciously.

"Well, I don't know," he pondered. "I guess I've discussed it in a general way with some of my close friends. They want to know what's made such a change in me these last few years. . . ."

All of these things, he explained, he'd pretty much figured out for himself—just checking on his own reactions and attitudes, recalling the things that had given him pleasure in the past, and noting how similar things provided no satisfaction now. It was all perfectly clear to him, and perfectly logical. And since he knew the nature of his trouble and understood himself so well, he didn't quite see what good a psychiatrist could be in his particular case.

"It's a kind of a rough deal on you, Doctor," he explained, almost sympathetically. "I already know the things you could spend weeks or months slowly finding out about me."

In that, he may have been correct. But if he did know them he wasn't admitting them, even to himself.

Under questioning, he insisted that he was perfectly satisfied with his position in the movie industry. He'd never been a top-flight star, or a major box-office attraction. But his name invariably appeared among the screen credits as an also-ran, or nearer to the top in second-rate productions.

"I wouldn't trade places with Clark Gable or Cary Grant or Jimmy Stewart for anything in the world," he insisted almost too vehemently. "They maybe make a little more money than I do, but they have a lot of headaches that I don't have to put up with. Besides, I have all the money I want and need, and a lot more than is really good for me. Why should I trade places with anybody?"

But in that he wasn't being entirely truthful with himself or with me, as we soon came to realize. The source of his trouble was something so obvious that it maybe could have been recognized by a reader of a movie fan magazine in Podunk. But Mr. C. had never found it in all his years of introspection—possibly because he didn't want to find it.

For years he had struggled to close that last gap, to rise from a B-grade movie actor to a top-flight star. During those years he had fought with his agents, switching from one agent to another—seeking always to find somebody who would push him up the final step to stardom. Three times during those years he had been married and divorced, with strong evidence that the matches had been inspired more by ambition than by genuine romance.

Finally had come a feeling of resignation and failure, and with it a loss of appetite for the struggle, and a prolonged melancholy mood. But such is the nature of unconscious self-deception that he'd never honestly admitted these things to himself, and certainly not to anyone else.

Ingeniously he'd placed it all upon a monetary basis while he subtly pointed out the moral to anyone who would listen: "I have more money now than is good for me. Why should I try to get more?" Like the fox in the fable, he'd decided that the inaccessible grapes were sour. And he'd added a footnote of his own: "Also, they give me indigestion and ruin my appetite."

Such is the value of introspection and self-analysis. We find only what we want to find, groping blindly past an unseen mountain in search of a remote little molehill.

Mr. C., fortunately, was a man of reasonable intelligence. And when he had at last honestly faced the cause of his morose discontent, he was ready to tackle a program of self-discipline and habit-substitution. It required nothing dramatic—merely the cultivation of interests beyond the limits of his own person.

Somewhere back along the line, some well-meaning friend had suggested that he should cultivate a hobby, and Mr. C. had acquired an enviable collection of miniatures which he enjoyed displaying. But in frank appraisal of the hobby, he conceded that it was merely another opportunity for personal exploitation. His primary interest was not in the miniatures themselves, but in the man who was able to indulge such an expensive whim. They were merely strategically placed mirrors to reflect additional glory upon himself.

"Have you ever done any fishing or hunting?" I inquired. But Mr. C. merely shuddered:

"Those things leave me perfectly cold."

And yet at my suggestion he made an honest attempt to cultivate an interest in these things in the months that followed, and with somewhat more than moderate success. For it has been my experience that persons in positions of respect need to cultivate hobbies where wealth and personal prestige are of no particular advantage. Even a B-grade movie actor or a second-flight executive with a generous expense account may be fawned over by head waiters, barbers, bell captains, and assorted hangers-on. But who ever heard of a deer or a trout or a jackrabbit being influenced by such nonsense?

Mr. C., I believe, was well on his way toward a more wholesome outlook on life and an intelligent program of habit-substitution, once he honestly faced the fact that he was only one of some two-thousand-million people scattered over the two-hundred-million square miles of this particular little globe hurtling through space and through the eons of time . . . and the reluctant realization that his particular career in Hollywood was not the only thing of possible importance, to him or to others.

Thinking mostly about one's self can get to be a habit, just like smoking cigarettes. But nicotine is by far the milder poison.

Instruments and gauges were placed on automotive dashboards for the convenience of motorists, and they can add to the safety of driving if properly used. But the man who concentrates his gaze upon the speedometer or the oil pressure gauge for great lengths of time may lose track of where he is going and wind up in the ditch. And similarly, the man who turns his thoughts ever inward, attempting to analyze each muscular twitch or each emotional reaction, may lose track of where he is going and end up with more trouble than all of that which he attempted to avoid.

The psychiatrist, like the plumber, may find his most difficult task is that of repairing the damage done by those who first tried to analyze the trouble and repair it themselves, before sending out for help.

I have never been willing to discard the hopeful little dreams of a better world of tomorrow, as first portrayed to me by the aging Dr. Beason. But gradually through the years I have changed my ideas of how it may possibly be achieved.

The final victory will not be won by the Flaming Sword of Knowledge striking down the last trace of ignorance. It will not be gained by men of science explaining to the masses how they must balance their meals and brush their teeth and swallow their vitamin pills. It will not be achieved by introspection, self-analysis, and the fascinating game of searching for symptoms.

For there is more to life than mere knowledge. And it is futile to become so absorbed in what a man has in his head, if we are to disregard what he has in his heart.

# 4

*Seems it strange that thou shouldst live forever? Is it less strange that thou shouldst live at all?—This is a miracle: and that no more.*—YOUNG

AMONG THE INCIDENTS of my boyhood that apparently would have been without significance if I had not followed through with a study of medicine and of psychiatry, was the episode of the bees.

Out back of the chicken coop on the farm, out in the midst of the aging orchard, there stood a half-dozen beehives. Once they'd been painted white, but the years had mouldered most of the paint away. Atop each hive stood a boulder to keep the lid in place. And close around the hives in the summer, the grass grew tall and untrammeled, for the man who mowed the orchard grass with a scythe maintained a discreet distance. In the fall the grass would be dry, and there would be the pungent odor of spoiling fruit which none had dared retrieve.

To me, the orchard was always a place of fascination. On warm summer days the busy buzzing was like a melody of contentment and the strange mixture of aromas was unbelievably pleasant. As a boy I collected my full quota of bee stings. But they never quite spoiled the allure.

Neither Mr. Burton nor any of the hands would venture near the hives and their periodic care was shouldered entirely by my father during his occasional visits to the farm. Usually at these times he would take me out to the orchard with him and Mr. Burton would dispatch one of the men to attend my usual chores. This, alone, would have been sufficient to inspire me with a fondness for the little insects.

But in addition, my father chose those occasions to enlighten me upon some of the broader facts of life. His knowledge of bees was remarkable and insofar as they were concerned, he was a romanticist. My first acute attack of puppy love was for a queen bee whose visible form I had never actually seen but whose regal presence within the hive could be safely assumed. She seemed to me the most glamorous figure imaginable.

Before our ventures out to the hives, my father and I had to climb into our outfits. Man-size gloves were pinned tightly to my shirt-sleeves, and a piece of mosquito netting was draped downward from the outer brim of my hat and fastened so that no bee could enter. The legs of my pants were brought down on the outside of my boots and firmly tied with twine. And if, in the end, I bore a slight resemblance to the scarecrow in the strawberry patch, it bothered me not at all, for my father was almost identically attired.

Always he carried a small smoke-belching bellows which he used to lull the bees into a stupor before the actual hive-robbing operation got under way. He cautioned me frequently against making any sudden moves that might startle the bees. And when he spoke, his voice was soft and low.

Quite casually he told me of the nuptial flight of the queen bee and it came as no particular surprise. The basic facts of life can hardly be hidden from view on a cattle ranch and there can be no mystery where there is no attempt to be mysterious.

But my father's story of the bees was far more than the usual birds-and-bees-and-spreading-of-pollen affair.

He told me how the queen bee returns to the hive and lays eggs inside the carefully prepared waxen cells; and how these hatch out to become special types of bees, each with its own particular work to do. He explained how some bees gather honey and others tend the young; how a few bees cater personally to the queen, like ladies-in-waiting; how the drones live a happy but useless life until one of them becomes the consort of the queen, only to plunge to earth dead when his mission in life is finished; and how the other drones are later driven from the hive to perish.

Among the waxen cells, he told me, there is one cell that is larger than the rest, and oval in shape. Here will be hatched the future queen. And there are special bees that stand guard over this royal cell from the moment the egg is deposited. They will, if necessary, even fight off the old queen, herself, in order to protect the royal lineage, and this situation is not uncommon. After depositing the egg, the queen has time to think the situation over and she commences to suspect that she hasn't been too smart about it all. A new and younger queen within the hive might complicate life considerably. So she strolls back to the oval-shaped incubator with murder in her heart and jealousy in her soul. But she is met and repulsed by the royal guards.

My father held the then-prevalent notion, subsequently proved incorrect, that the queen could decide, arbitrarily, just what kind of egg she wanted to lay next. This was the simple answer to the rather involved question of how a perfect balance is maintained within the hive, with just the proper ratio of bees in each respective trade. It also answered the question of how the queen, with unerring accuracy, was able to deposit the royal egg within the prearranged royal cell— a rather neat mystery in itself.

Late one afternoon when my father was absent from the farm I returned from the back pastureland with the cattle to find Uncle Charlie hopping with excitement.

"Your bees has gone crazy," he shouted. "They've swarmed all over the back porch and Chinaman Charlie locked the door and won't open it, and there ain't gonna be no supper, less'n we can get them dratted things out'n there!"

Mr. Burton and several of the hands were standing out behind the house when I came running up, viewing the situation from a safe distance. On the back porch stood a long wooden wash bench atop which sat the granite wash pans and the bars of home-made soap. But now one end of the bench was covered by a solid swarming mass of bees. The ominous humming could be heard at considerable distance. And their bodies, pressed tightly together, formed an ill-defined mass that hung downward almost like a bunch of grapes.

"They're swarming," I announced with sudden pride in my vast knowledge. "The queen bee is right inside the swarm, and the other bees have gathered around to protect her. This is the only time the queen bee leaves the hive except for the nuptial flight." But nobody seemed particularly impressed with my extemporaneous lecture.

"What do we do with them?" Mr. Burton asked uneasily. "They can't stay there."

"When bees swarm," I explained, "it is a very good time to move them to a new hive, my father says. The reason why they swarm is because they got too crowded in the old hive. A new queen is growing up and the old queen has been forced out to find a new home."

"Well she can't make her new home on the wash bench," Mr. Burton concluded sadly. "And besides, we haven't got any new hive. How long will they stay there if we just leave them alone?"

But that, unfortunately, was one of the things my father hadn't told me. And having exhausted my store of knowledge, I stood viewing the situation as dismally as the rest.

"If I could get inside the house and get my bee outfit," I offered, "I could pick them up and carry them back to one of the old hives."

After very short deliberation Mr. Burton decided that this was probably the only wise answer. But it took a prolonged negotiation and a fiery ultimatum from Mr. Burton to get Chinaman Charlie to unlock the front door of the house with so many bees close at hand.

Once completely pinned and tied inside my weird outfit, I walked calmly up to the bench and attempted to pick up the swarm. The effect was unlike anything I had expected. Their tiny bodies, clinging together, congealed them into a single mass. They were unbelievably warm and soft. And walking slowly out toward the orchard it seemed almost as if I were carrying a loudly purring kitten in my arms. Bees may be plural. But a swarm of bees is somehow singular.

Many years later in a classroom at Harvard, I sat and listened to a professor explaining how different cells are formed within the human body, each with its own specific work to do. And as I listened, I couldn't help noticing that it was an old, familiar story—being run through with a different cast. Here, basically, was the same story my father had told me years ago. Only instead of being the story of bees, this was the story of living cells. Whereas bees swarm and form a single congealed mass only on occasion, the cells of the body cling together all through life—which greatly simplifies the task of the census-taker.

Just as some bees are destined to gather honey, while others tend the young, or serve the queen, or live as drones; so are the various cells of the body destined to do their highly specialized jobs within the complex, skin-covered human beehive.

And just as the suddenly jealous queen bee may attempt to destroy the future queen after having deposited the egg, and just as she is driven off by the royal guards, so do conflicts exist within the human body. Deep and hidden conflicts. For even though the living cells are highly organized and interdependent and all on the same team, so to speak—yet each is primarily concerned with its individual destiny.

Sometimes I suspect that we could better understand the nature of our mortal bodies and the complexities of psychic life, if the various cells that compose us didn't stick quite so closely together—if they could just fly off in various directions like a batch of bees at blossom time. For then, surely, we would understand that man is not a single organism but a highly complex society of smaller organisms bunched up together for the common good . . . or the common peril.

It is the belief of many men today that all life started with the simple cell, of which all living matter is composed. Only somewhere back in the dark eons of the past, certain cells found that they could fare better by sticking together than by shifting individually for themselves. So they formed a corporation and the first multicell organism began. In the new corporation, each cell had its own specialized work to do and there came the first effort toward coöperative efficiency: "You bring in the food. I'll take care of the kids. And Joe, here, will carry out the garbage."

The nature of life and of living cells can readily be understood by considering a simple organism that has been content to remain a simple organism down through the ages—such as the amoeba.

An amoeba is a tiny one-cell critter without sex or social inhibitions. It reproduces its kind by merely dividing across the middle, like a lady of the wasp-waist era who'd drawn her corset strings too tight. When the hourglass figure divides completely, the upper portion and the lower portion both swim away and each is an amoeba in its own right. Eventually these will also divide. And a man could go crazy trying to figure out the family relationship. Is the upper half the parent of the lower half? Or vice versa? Or both? Are the newly divided amoebas actually brothers and sisters, like a couple of surgically divided Siamese twins? Or are they still, basically, the same original amoeba?

Strictly speaking, one amoeba is related to another amoeba in the same way that he is related to himself. In at least one sense, the grand patriarch of the entire amoeba species is still living. Through a prolonged process of short division, he has now covered most of the world and you can find living offshoots of the old boy practically anywhere that fresh water is to be found.

The amoeba and other unicellular organisms suffer distinct disadvantages because of their grim determination to stick to the simple life. From the standpoint of man, their life appears almost too simple to be interesting. No sin. No sex. No sentiment. No proud family lineage.

But in exchange for this, the unicellular organisms enjoy certain peculiar advantages. They hold the secret of life eternal. In laboratory studies spanning thousands upon thousands of generations there was found not one instance of "natural death" among a culture of one-cell animals.

There emerges then the grave suspicion that man's ailments are of a corporate nature. The individual cells that compose the body hold a certain potential immortality. But as a group they eventually fail in their coöperative enterprise.

In a physical way, the cells of the human body no doubt suffer from being fenced in. They are surrounded above and below and on all sides by other cells of the body, and the potential growth of the individual reaches a statute of limitations. This is in sharp contrast to the free-lance amoeba in the middle of the lake with the entire world as potential growing room.

In a series of remarkable experiments with rats, it has been demonstrated that the unmistakable signs of old age commence to appear when growing stops. In theory, at least, man would continue to live for a thousand years if he could continue to grow for a thousand years.

In a psychological way, the cells of the body no doubt suffer from a lack of esprit de corps. It is difficult to keep a baseball team "sharp" for an entire season. One man may go into a batting slump and his depression may spread to others. And the first thing you know the entire team is in the doldrums. Is it illogical to assume that the cells composing the human body suffer from an inability to remain "sharp" indefinitely? The enthusiasm to Do or Die for dear old Rutgers may eventually commence to wane.

There are problems of management and of interdependence in the multicell organism that the unicellular organism never has to reckon with.

The development of man from a single cell in the eons of the past, or from a single cell within the womb, might be compared to the development of a modern shoe factory. The history of the firm starts with old Grandpa Schultz who made shoes by hand. He was a single individual and the responsibility was his alone. He could set his own pace and establish his own standards. But he soon discovered that he could do better by hiring a helper, and from that day on he wasn't quite so independent. He had to be sure to have the shop open by the time the helper arrived. Through the years and through successive generations the firm continued to grow until it became a great sprawling factory covering many acres and employing thousands. But now, each worker has one highly specialized job to do. And each, in a way, is dependent upon the rest. When the Heel Fitters and Tongue Sewers Local 107 goes out on strike, the entire plant must eventually close down, for there's no sense making shoes without heels or tongues. When there's a railroad strike or a meat packers' strike, or a jurisdictional dispute in the warehouse, the entire plant is affected and production must be curtailed. There is no longer the independence that Grandpa Schultz knew when he had a keg of nails under his workbench, a stack of cowhides on the shelf, and a steady market among his neighbors.

When the living cells of the human animal tossed in their lot together—when they formed their complex corporation—they signed away their chances for immortality. They insured that the entire body would suffer from the failings of any organ in the anatomy and they accepted the inevitable fact that a chain is no stronger than its weakest link. In seeking the "better life" of which only a higher type of animal is capable, man, himself, became expendable.

Slowly but surely we are learning that there are certain definite patterns to the universe that repeat themselves again and again.

As we have learned more about the atom we have come to visualize it as an entire universe in miniature, with its infinitesimal planets pursuing their prescribed courses like a scale model of the very heavens we have studied through the centuries.

The relationship of man to the society in which he lives, bears a striking similarity to the relationship of the cell toward the body, or the bee toward the hive. Each cell has its own particular work to do for the benefit of the body as a whole. And when it fails to do that work it is not a healthy cell. And to that identical extent, it is not a healthy body.

Each living person likewise has his own particular work to do for the benefit of society as a whole. He has his own contributions to make. And if he fails in this he is not an emotionally healthy person. And to that degree it is not a healthy society.

Of the thousands of mentally and emotionally abnormal persons I have observed in more than half a century, I believe the one most frequent denominator among them has been a lack of worthy purpose in life . . . a lack of ambition or a lack of opportunity to be of some definite purpose in society; to make some definite and at least partially unselfish contribution to the world.

A friend of mine—a practicing physician who never misses an opportunity to ridicule psychiatry, half in fun and half in earnest—once told me that he had one standard prescription for folks who complain of aches and pains when he can find nothing physically wrong:

"I work hell out of 'em," he told me, grinning. "I make 'em bring me a schedule of what they do every hour of the day. And no matter what it says on the schedule, I tell 'em they're taking life too easy. I get 'em to join the Red Cross, solicit funds for the Community Chest, lead a Boy Scout troop—anything to keep 'em busy and to keep 'em from sitting around and moping about their miseries." And he challenged me to compare results, on a percentage basis.

"I'll bet you, sight unseen," he challenged, "that I can show as good a percentage of recoveries as any psychiatrist in the country. And I charge 'em five bucks for an office call, instead of twenty-five, or fifty!" Nor did I make any effort to call his bet.

It was, of course, an unfair challenge. The few slightly neurotic persons calling at his office, complaining of an assortment of aches and pains, are not to be compared with the advanced psychotics who trudge in endless numbers into the offices of psychiatrists. But he had a good point, possibly better than he realized.

The need to serve society is not mere "busy-work," to keep the mind off aches and pains. It is a necessary outlet to give life meaning, and to make it satisfying. It is a prerequisite to endowing human life with simple dignity . . . to place man above the status of old Maud whom Uncle Charlie aptly described as having nothing to look forward to, " 'cept some day bein' driv' to the slaughter house."

A life without purpose is but aimless wandering along the path that leads to the grave. And who could rightfully expect it to be rich in satisfaction?

But mental abnormality is not stereotyped, and the keep-busy therapy has its limitations. There came the day when my optimistic friend confessed that his system had failed.

"It's a very odd case," he told me. "This woman has asthma attacks almost every afternoon. And what's odd about it, they always come at four o'clock. Never miss by more than five minutes either way."

The patient, Mrs. G., it developed, had even less faith in psychiatry than did her physician. For when he later suggested that she visit me, she irately refused. "After all, I'm not just imagining these attacks, Doctor," she protested. "Don't be so foolish as to suggest it's all in my mind."

It was in the spring of the year and we decided, then, to give Mrs. G. a little more time to see if she might change her attitude. And then one day, quite casually, the physician asked her if she'd noticed any change in the frequency or in the timing of the attacks. She hadn't.

"Doesn't it seem rather odd," he asked her, "that your attacks would know how to shift over to daylight saving time?"

This, oddly enough, she had not even considered. But she was far from convinced. It should be noted, also, that the attacks occurred at four o'clock regardless of where she was or what she chanced to be doing at the time.

"Sometimes," she announced triumphantly, "there won't be a clock in the room where I am. I won't be wearing my watch, and I'll have lost all track of time. But I'll feel my attack coming on, and then when I go in another room and look at the clock, it'll be just four o'clock!"

"The thing's got me beat," her physician told me. "I'd wash my hands of it and insist that she find herself a new doctor since she won't let me call in anybody else. But the thing fascinates me."

At his insistence, he told me, Mrs. G. had thrown herself whole-heartedly into a program of club work and social service, but in this case it didn't help.

"What I can't figure out is this," he told me. "If she really loses track of the time, as she says, and if there's no clock in the room, and if the cause of the attack is something psychological, then how come it shows up at exactly four o'clock?"

But to answer that question, one must consider the very peculiar working agreement that exists among the cells that constitute the human body. In the fields of transportation, communication, self-government, national defense, priority rationing, and a host of other things, they have somehow worked out a program of coöperative enterprise which, for efficiency, surpasses anything we have ever read about in our newspapers or in our history books.

To solve the mystery of the four o'clock deadline, one must first face an even greater mystery—that of the subconscious mind, or the unconscious, if you prefer. Like Santa Claus, Kris Kringle, or St. Nicholas, it's known by many different names. And like Santa Claus, also, its nature, its identity, and its very existence are open to question in many quarters.

# 5

*It is with disease of the mind, as with those of the body: we are half dead before we understand our disorder, and half cured when we do.*—COLTON

WITH ALL DUE respect to such men as Freud, James, Wundt, Titchener and Thorndike, it remains my firm belief that Alexander Graham Bell made perhaps the greatest single contribution to our general understanding of psychic phenomena.

Never to my knowledge have I read a beginner's textbook on psychology that did not compare the nervous system to a telephone company. And I have often wondered how the subject could even be approached if the telephone had never been invented?

In the early days of my professorship in Los Angeles I discovered that a number of students from more isolated Western areas were entirely unfamiliar with the telephone. And it always seemed practical at the start of the semester to devote several days to a discussion of telephone service so that the traditional comparisons could later be made.

I have often suspected that my short and ill-fated sojourn at M.I.T. left more of an impression upon me than it ever left upon the school. Often I find myself surveying medical or psychological problems from a mechanical or engineering standpoint.

I am sure the old basic comparison of the nervous system to the telephone company must be familiar to most people. In this, the nerves are pictured as telephone lines running to all parts of the anatomy while the brain represents central's office. If the individual inadvertently places his hand upon a hot stove, a little nerve ending immediately dashes into a convenient phone booth and commences dialing frantically:

"Hello, Operator? This is the index finger of the left hand reporting. It's hotter'n hades down here."

In the brain, central promptly springs into action as prescribed in Section 22-W, covering emergencies. She flips a switch turning on the speakers in the front office. She pushes and pulls cords like mad and barks out orders to the various muscles of the body. To the big muscles of the upper arm she suggests, "Better pull yourselves together, Boys. We want to lift the left hand straight upward." Similar orders go out to the muscles of the legs, back, neck, abdomen, and even the tongue, cheeks, and lips, plus a host of internal organs and mechanisms.

Through the contraction and expansion of strategically located muscles, the body straightens up and a foot stamps the floor; the injured finger darts upward and in and out of the mouth and then the entire hand is waved frantically in mid-air. The vocal cords vibrate and the oral cavity shapes the basic tone into short, staccato, significant sounds: "Who in the hell left the heat turned on in that front burner?"

It is all beautifully coördinated and of course it takes place in far less time than it takes to explain it. But every tiniest movement is performed by muscles getting their orders by remote control from the nerve centers of the brain. Central has the situation well in hand—like Cousin Elmer operating the Giant Claw machine at Frisby's Drug Store.

This telephonic comparison is unusually apt. Nerve cells of the body bear a physical resemblance to tiny, insulated telephone lines and there is evidence that their impulses are electrical in nature. Nearly every high school student has seen the muscles of a frog's leg contract under an electrical impact from a battery. The ability of living cells to generate electricity is well established and at a recent World's Fair a radio receiving set was operated by the electricity produced by living organisms. A number of scientists today are pursuing the theory that the mystery of life and the mystery of electricity are one and the same, and that the human lifeline is nothing more and nothing less than the allotment of so many kilowatt hours.

As for the aforementioned comparison of the nervous system to a local telephone company, it has often seemed to me in later years that the comparison is not carried far enough in our schools and colleges. It is perfectly obvious that a telephone company doesn't operate with just a batch of pay phones and one operator on duty. Who's going to send out the monthly bills? Who's going to keep track of the charges on toll calls? Who's going to sell the ads in the yellow section of the directory? Who's going to figure out the withholding tax on the operators' salary? There are many details that must be attended to in the operation of a telephone company, aside from merely placing calls. And similarly, there are infinite details that must be attended to in the operation of the human body, aside from pulling fingers away from hot stoves. Possibly it would better explain the complicated psychic process if the illustration were carried to its ultimate conclusion.

Back in the days of the old-fashioned party line, Grandpa Scroggins might dash to his phone and ring the operator to report that his barn was ablaze, and to ask her to please call the volunteer fire department. But even before the first gong was struck on the fire bell in town, neighbors might come dashing up from all directions armed with buckets and shovels and prepared to fight the fire.

How'd they know about it so soon? Grandpa Scroggins was too polite to ask, but the answer was fairly obvious: They'd been listening in on the party line.

Similarly, in cases of emergency, the muscles of the body may respond even before the brain has time to weigh the situation and bark out orders. These instantaneous responses are known as reflex actions. If, for some fabulous reason, a person gritted his teeth and determined to hold his hand indefinitely on a hot stove, he would find it almost impossible to do so . . . just as Grandpa Scroggins would find it impossible to make his neighbors stay home while his barn blazed dramatically in the night sky.

But it's at the headquarters of the telephone company that the most interesting procedures take place.

Imagine yourself, now, as the General Manager of a local telephone company with thousands of subscribers. In planning the layout of the building it would be quite apparent that you couldn't have your desk in the same room with all the operators. How could you ever concentrate with all that racket going on? "Number please." "What number were you calling?" "At the tone, the time will be 9:23 and one quarter." "I'm sorry, that phone has been disconnected." In such an atmosphere you couldn't hear yourself think.

It's quite obvious that your executive office will have to be up in the front of the building with a few good soundproof partitions. To do your best executive work, you need to get away from these infinite, trivial details.

And so it is that the conscious mind is separated from the subconscious mind. While you're sitting and figuring your income tax with the aid of your conscious mind, the subconscious mind out in the back room is taking care of the routine details—keeping the lungs breathing and the digestion operating, and so on. Without being aware of what you're doing, you may reach up and switch a fly away from the back of your neck. This is because the subconscious mind attends to the details. "Aw shucks, no sense bothering the boys in the front office when they're busy. I'll just handle it myself." The Chief Operator of the subconscious mind is not only a trusted employee of long standing, but also a major stockholder in the company. She takes more and more responsibilities unto herself.

Somewhere in the back room, but easily accessible from the executive offices, must be the file cabinets of memory. Here, for future reference, are filed thousands of dates, names, incidents, and telephone numbers. If they are filed carefully and painstakingly, many can be found when needed. If they are tossed helter-skelter into any drawer that happens to be open, there is less chance that they'll be found promptly when required. And as in any filing system, the more recent additions are generally the easiest to locate.

But did you ever notice how comparatively helpless is the typical executive trying to find a certain letter on his secretary's day off? Because he does not daily attend these routine details, he is not entirely proficient at the task. And similarly, the subconscious mind may have access to memory factors which elude the conscious mind.

There are, of course, bad days in every line of business. When things start going wrong at the telephone company, the Manager gets out his manual or handbook and attempts to find an immediate solution to the problem, possibly working overtime and instituting new measures of company policy. If these things fail to work and if the situation grows progressively worse, he must eventually call in a trained trouble-shooter.

When an individual becomes aware of the improper functioning of his mind or body, he turns first and most logically to an attempted self-diagnosis with the aid of his self-help magazines, a Home Doctor Book, and the advice of Mrs. Murphy generously tendered over the back fence. There may follow gallant attempts to turn over a new leaf and to live a new life. But the mirror of introspection, unfortunately, reflects everything in reverse, and a physician is generally capable of safeguarding everyone's health but his own. Usually, after this self-diagnosis has failed and his home remedies have proved futile, the individual seeks the services of a medical trouble-shooter.

Ordinarily the problem is taken first to the family physician who searches for symptoms of a pathological nature. He has devoted his life to that particular branch of medical science in which he is engaged. He believes in it, usually, with all his heart and soul. And he may be understandably reluctant to pass the problem along like an unsolved puzzle without a conscientious attempt to solve it, personally. Quite often he, too, must try and fail before the problem reaches the psychiatrist. You'd be surprised how few patients ever reach a psychiatrist's office with their tonsils, wisdom teeth, or vermiform appendix still intact. These things are often parted with in the preliminary attempt to find the key to the puzzle before the psychiatrist is called in.

And yet even though the problem may be one requiring the service of a psychiatrist, it is far from being solved when the patient actually enters the psychiatrist's office. Because of ridiculous and widespread misunderstanding and misconception, the average man in the street may dread his appointment with the psychiatrist just slightly less than he dreads his eventual appointment with the undertaker. He resents the imagined implication of such a visit. And he may answer questions with as much coöperative spirit as a two-time loser facing a third degree. There is perhaps no trouble-shooter in any other line of endeavor who receives less volunteer coöperation from his customers at the outset. And there is none who needs it more.

Our aforementioned trouble-shooter at the telephone company is generally greeted with a frank recital of all known difficulties: "When our subscribers dial Dr. Smith's office, they invariably get the Curator at the zoo. When we plug in for a long distance call to Albuquerque, the entire conversation is heard over all the radio receiving sets in the community." These things the trouble-shooter considers thoughtfully. He scratches his chin, and studies the diagram of the master switchboard. He maybe disconnects a few wires experimentally and then solders them together again. But eventually he traces down the source of the trouble: "There's a short circuit inside the cable leading to the transformer." And once the source of the trouble is located, it remains merely a routine task to correct it.

In much the same way, the psychiatrist attempts to trace the source of trouble in the subconscious mind. If he attempts psychoanalysis, he is handicapped by the patient's unwillingness to discuss his innermost thoughts, and a great amount of time is spent in gaining the patient's confidence and in breaking down the barriers of vocal inhibition. He is handicapped by the lack of any master diagram or chart, for each subconscious mind is purely a custom job, wired and woven about the experiences of the individual. He is handicapped by the lack of a mental soldering iron, for he cannot in conscience resort to surgery for experimental purposes.

And yet, through patient and prolonged effort, the psychoanalyst may be able to isolate the source of trouble within the subconscious mind. And once this is located, the entire problem is at least fifty percent solved.

It should be specifically understood that these comparisons to a telephone office constitute a functional illustration and are not intended as a lesson in anatomy. There is no specific area of the brain that is clearly defined as the subconscious mind. There are no actual partitions lined with Celotex. No desk, chairs, or carpets. And if these disclaimers seem superfluous, I should explain that they are necessary for the benefit of certain literal-minded critics who deny the existence of a subconscious mind because they are unable to pick it up with a pair of tweezers from the brain of a cadaver.

But even the critics, in the midst of their profound statements, are not consciously recalling the square root of sixteen or the name of Uncle Herman's second wife, although they may be able to recall these things when the occasion arises. All of us, critics and criticized alike, are subject to moods and emotions and tensions which bear no apparent relationship to our conscious thoughts. And we may be able, today, to remember something that we couldn't remember yesterday.

Of this there can be no argument: There is more to the psychic phenomenon than the conscious thoughts of any particular moment. And whether we choose to call it memory, habit, the subconscious, the unconscious, the reactive, or endow it with a simple little name like Elmer, the basic fact of its existence is hardly subject to intelligent denial.

It has always seemed to me that there is sufficient room for debate as to the nature of this below-the-level-of-consciousness phenomenon without quibbling over what to call it.

Once Mrs. G. had been finally induced to try psychiatric help in seeking the cause of her four o'clock attacks of asthma, I promptly attempted to trace any incidents, emotions, or reactions that could be associated with the onset of the series of attacks. When this proved futile, I endeavored to learn if the hour of four o'clock held any significance in her life that she could recall.

"I used to have a favorite radio program that came on at four o'clock," she told me thoughtfully. "I always tried to remember to tune it in. But it's been off the air for months."

There, obviously, was a clue. And it was followed down methodically. But sad to say, not all clues lead to pay dirt, as do those in a mystery novel. Mrs. G.'s efforts to recall thoughts and impressions associated with the radio program eventually led exactly nowhere. Gradually she recalled other things: Her youngest daughter had been born at just a few minutes after four. She recalled various appointments she'd had at four o'clock during her life—incidents that she hadn't recalled in years. And then, eventually, she recalled that four o'clock had been her deadline for getting home from school when she was a girl.

"My mother was awfully strict about it," she recalled. "She insisted that four o'clock didn't mean ten minutes after four, or even two minutes after four. If I wasn't actually inside the house, or at least coming up our front walk when the hall clock struck four, I wasn't permitted to go anywhere to play for a whole week."

One incident in particular she recalled, after putting her mind to it. It was to have been her first afternoon of freedom after a week of confinement within her own yard, and she had made elaborate plans at school to visit a particularly close friend, who was arranging an impromptu party. She had hurried directly home from school and then stood in dismayed horror to see the hall clock somberly proclaiming two minutes after four.

"The clock is fast," she'd screamed. "It must be fast. The big clock on the Court House said a quarter to four, and I hurried straight home."

But her mother had stood stern and unrelenting. "If the clock is fast now, it must have been fast when you left for school this morning. I haven't touched it. And you know as well as I do, that this is the clock we go by." She had then delivered a lecture on promptness, self-reliance, and planning ahead for all eventualities. And there had followed another week of confinement inside the yard.

This incident Mrs. G. insisted she hadn't thought about in years.

"It seems rather odd that anything like that, which must have made quite an impression on you at the time, wouldn't be recalled now and then in thinking back on your childhood," I suggested. But she shook her head.

"I didn't have a particularly happy childhood," she told me. "I don't spend much time sitting around and thinking about it."

And with that came the suspicion that pay dirt couldn't be far away. It developed that Mrs. G., as a girl, had built up a hatred for her mother who was an uncompromising disciplinarian. But it hadn't been a simple, all-out hatred. It had been mixed in with love, also, and a sense of shame. For even a little girl realizes that it isn't proper for her to hate her own mother.

I noticed that Mrs. G. was reluctant to speak of her mother as our interviews progressed. She would adroitly change the subject, which was the strongest clue of all. But eventually the whole story unfolded.

Her mother, at the time of our interviews, was living in a distant state and receiving state funds for the care of the needy aged. During the previous year it had been necessary for Mrs. G. to sign an affidavit that she was financially unable to contribute toward her mother's support, and this had weighed heavily upon her conscience. Actually, Mrs. G. was reasonably well-to-do. Her husband was an executive in a large retail firm, but she hadn't felt that she could ask him to send money to her mother each month. The inevitable result had been emotional conflict.

Consciously, Mrs. G. hadn't recalled her daily four o'clock deadline as a small girl. But the memory had been retained all that time in her subconscious mind. And the ability of the subconscious mind to keep track of time, even without an alarm clock, is almost fantastic.

The man who is accustomed to going to bed at ten o'clock and getting up at six, is obviously accustomed to getting eight hours' sleep each night. But on one night he doesn't get to bed until midnight. So does he sleep on through until eight o'clock in the morning, thus getting his accustomed eight hours' sleep? No. Not ordinarily. He still awakens at six. And who, I wonder, has not set the alarm for four o'clock to get an early start for a fishing trip or some such thing, only to awaken and stare at the clock five minutes before the alarm is set to ring? Even without a clock, or a candle, or an hourglass, and even in the inky blackness of the darkest night, the subconscious mind somehow makes its accurate measurements of time. Through acquired habit, hooked up to the same internal time mechanism, the factory worker may daily hear the first bid of a sudden mid-day appetite at precisely five minutes to twelve.

The fact that Mrs. G. should experience an asthma attack at four o'clock in the afternoon, even when she couldn't see a clock and had consciously lost all track of time, was in itself a strong hint of some earlier habit-pattern of which she was no longer conscious. Even though the be-home-from-school deadline no longer existed, the subconscious mind had apparently remained faithful to its once-assigned duty, all through the years.

Reverting to the illustration of the telephone company, we can commence to visualize Mrs. G.'s emotional conflict if we envision her subconscious thoughts as the comments of several operators discussing the situation:

"It's just about four o'clock," says one. "She's going to catch holy Ned from her mother if she's not home by the time the clock strikes. And you gals better get braced for an emergency."

"No, that's not true any more," says another one. "She's a grown woman now and she has a home of her own, and she doesn't have to account to her mother for her actions."

"Speaking of her mother," chimes in a third, "she's certainly a hard-hearted old witch if I ever heard of one. I understand she's living on relief, or some such thing, and it certainly serves her right."

"Yes, but just the same it's still her mother," replies the second operator. "What would it hurt her to send the old lady a few dollars every month? Really, sometimes I wish she'd choke, going around from house to house asking people to contribute to charity, when her own poor old mother has to shop around and buy day-old bread."

And at about this point of the subconscious conflict, Mrs. G. actually did choke each afternoon. She'd gasp for breath, and fight her way toward a chair, and signal her daughter to put in another call to the poor, harassed physician. Meanwhile she might mix and swallow an evil-smelling potion, while gasping indignantly:

"If he thinks this is all in my mind, I wish he'd have one of these attacks. Just once. Then he'd know I'm not imagining it."

And she was, of course, one hundred percent correct in her conviction that her attacks weren't imaginary. The suffering was real. The agony was genuine.

But how could an emotional conflict—mere subconscious thoughts, you might say—cause suffering that's real?

To answer that, it is necessary to go into one other phase of the psychosomatic entity—the inseparable and indistinguishable mind and body of man.

# 6

*Indigestion is charged by God with enforcing morality
on the stomach.*—HUGO

THERE IS A tendency today to consider psychosomatic medicine as
something ultramodern. It is in reality very old—much older than our
concepts of bacterial infection. Basically, it is the realization that the
mind and the body of man are tied irrevocably together, and that it
will prove more confusing than enlightening to consider one while
disregarding the other. The word "psychosomatic" is in itself a neat
job of word-root welding, drawn from "psyche" meaning mind, and
"soma" meaning body.

Primitive man made little attempt to separate mind and body, for his
analytical thinking hadn't progressed to the point where he could
tackle such a complicated task of division.

Through the eons of the past, medicine men have given greater or
lesser attention to the mind, the soul, or the spirit of man, attempting
to combat human ailments with a varying hodge-podge of herbs,
prayers, and boiled buffalo horns; rhythmic dances around the campfire and sacrifices to the gods; steam-baths and bloodletting, and bowing low toward the East. And the men of one generation have laughed
derisively at the silly superstitions of the generations of the past.

I spent my early life with my father's philosophy ringing in my
ears; the happy belief that a healthy mind is a natural by-product of
a healthy body.

During my early medical studies at Harvard I learned that the body
is an intricate mechanical contraption fighting valiantly for survival in

66

the midst of a world filled with germs, poisons, runaway horses, and other things grimly intent upon its destruction. I learned, almost as a side issue, that the presence of pathological ailments may cause a patient to feel morose and perhaps a little frightened, and that it's the physician's Christian and neighborly duty to say a few words to cheer him up.

During my early studies in Vienna I learned, inversely, that man is basically a psychic entity. I was given a personal introduction to the Chief Operator of the subconscious mind, and I was given to understand that muscles and fibers and tendons are little more than the strings of her puppet show. As a man thinketh, so is he. Later, with a complete reversal of almost everything I had learned before, I was informed that pathological ailments, in large measure, are merely the visible symptoms of something gone wrong in the psychic process: Find and correct the trouble in the subconscious mind, and the pathological ailments will often take care of themselves.

During the early days of my general practice in Los Angeles, I found myself in a highly peculiar position. I was a psychiatrist by choice, and a practicing physician through the pressure of economic necessity. There weren't enough calls for psychiatric help to keep me busy. During those days I kept two complete sets of office stationery; one set including the word "Psychiatrist," and the other set carefully deleting it. And I lived in daily dread of ever leaving any stationery exposed in my office, for some of my more cautious and conservative medical patients would perhaps have fled in terror at the very sight of the word. "My dear, I just happened to find out: The man is a mystic and a faith-healer. I saw the term 'Psychiatrist' on his stationery!"

But even more disturbing than this was the matter of my own philosophy. How could I be a psychiatrist in the morning, dedicated to the belief that certain pathological ailments are the direct result of mental or emotional conflict, and then in the afternoon become a practicing physician, accepting the premise that the human body is an elaborate organic mechanism, and that emotions and attitudes are largely the by-products of pathological stimulus? Specifically, how could I explain to Mr. Smith in the morning, "Your ulcers are the result of too much nervous tension," and then explain to Mr. Jones in the afternoon, "Your nervous tension is the result of having ulcers"?

Fortunately, at about this point I bought my first automobile and received my first basic training in mechanical first aid. Service stations, then, were practically unknown. Gasoline was usually dispensed from single pumps in front of general mercantile stores. Garages were few and far between, and blacksmiths, generally, were eager but ill informed. When a motorist got beyond the limits of the city, he was largely dependent upon his own mechanical ingenuity to keep the car running.

I learned, then, quickly to diagnose automotive troubles as one of two varieties: They were either mechanical or electrical. The test was simple but hazardous: I would carefully wrap a wooden-handled screwdriver inside a handkerchief, and span the metal blade from the top of a spark plug to the top of the engine block, while somebody turned the crank. If I could see sparks jump as the crank turned, or if I picked myself up out of the ditch while ruefully recalling that I'd absent-mindedly touched the fender during the process, then I knew that the difficulty was mechanical, and probably centered somewhere near the carburetor. If there was no spark, then I knew the trouble was electrical and it could generally be repaired by tracking down a loose wire or rendering a highly specialized type of coil-box manicure, with the aid of a fingernail file.

But for me, and apparently for thousands of others in the medical field, it served a more far-reaching purpose. Here, surely, was the perfect example of how the ailments of mankind could be divided. Some ailments may be considered mechanical—or pathological—and they may be treated with the long familiar and standardized medical technique. Some ailments may be considered electrical—or psychogenic —and they may be treated with psychiatry.

And so it remained through many years that medical men divided human ailments into the two categories, searching always for some simple test like the screwdriver-across-the-spark plug technique, to determine whether a specific malady was pathological or psychogenic. Most of the years of my professional practice were dedicated to this premise. And even in the days following World War I, when the increasing demand for psychiatric help made it possible for me to dispense with bone-setting and delivering babies and to devote my full time to psychiatry, there remained the almost-taken-for-granted belief that human ailments could be neatly divided into the two convenient and distinct categories.

But then, belatedly, and with a rare burst of insight, it suddenly occurred to somebody that men and automobiles, after all, are not identical. There came the suggestion that possibly man had been wasting his time through the years, attempting to trace the dividing line between pathological and psychogenic maladies, and striving to determine which was responsible for the other in each specific case.

Even though I had passed my allotted three-score-and-ten, and even though this premise struck at the convictions I had held through a large share of my lifetime, still the basic tenets seemed intriguing. And at about this time I chanced to learn that medical men in Lima, Peru, were hopping with excitement over their achievements with psychosomatic medicine. The national university in Lima, (which, incidentally, is older than Harvard) in cooperation with the Obreros Hospital, had established a department for the study of functional disturbances, and medical men from all parts of the world were assembling there in international convention to observe the progress that had been made. And so I made arrangements once again to leave my home, not only to attend the convention but to spend a year in study and practice at the Obreros Hospital. This move on my part was bitterly opposed by my family and I'm afraid it was generally misunderstood by my friends.

As gently and as adroitly as they could, they pointed out that I was an old man, and that the sands were running low in the hourglass of time. Subtly, they explained that these newer therapies should be explored by younger men who have a lifetime of practice before them, and who can put their knowledge to some practical use. There is little purpose studying the spring seed catalogues so late in the fall.

My motives, of course, were entirely selfish. And I attempted to justify them with the argument that an old man should be permitted to indulge his whims. I had no illusions, this time, of rectifying all that was wrong with the world, or of personally carrying the bright light of reason into the dark recesses of ignorance and folly. It was merely that I had grown intrigued by the plot of a fascinating story that had started among the beehives on the farm in the days of my youth. And I couldn't resist the opportunity to read the next thrilling episode, even though it called for one more trip to another continent. I paid my own way, and I consoled myself with the knowledge that my trip deprived no younger man of a similar opportunity. There were empty staterooms on the boat, and vacant hotel rooms in Lima.

In much the same way that the invention of the telephone made it possible for man to visualize the functioning of the nervous system, so did the development of the peptic ulcer make it possible for man to comprehend the basic premise of psychiatry. It is perhaps the simplest illustration of how an actual, pathological ailment may develop from an emotional disturbance.

The stomach can be compared to a rather crude version of our modern automatic washing machine, without the glass door or the chrome trim. It tumbles the food around and, instead of injecting soap chips and changing rinse water, it injects certain gastric juices provided by other nearby digestive organs. This is all fully automatic, and is of inestimable convenience to the busy housewife. She can even put on her coat and hat and go shopping while her internal Bendix does its work.

Only it isn't always that simple. It takes energy to operate the stomach just as it takes electrical energy to operate an automatic washing machine. And the human body is forever faced with the problem of a potential power shortage. In times of emergency the Chief Operator of the subconscious mind shuts down all noncritical operations so that the full supply of the body's energy may be available for the more crucial tasks at hand. It is a rationing program on the basis of first things first.

Strong emotions of fear or anger are considered emergencies so far as the body is concerned and it immediately goes upon an emergent wartime basis. The digestive process is brought to a halt as the tempo of the heartbeat and respiration increases and added amounts of adrenalin are pumped into the bloodstream. The body is prepared for fight or for flight. The final decision will probably be made by the conscious mind. But whichever pathway is chosen, the Chief Operator of the subconscious mind wants the body prepared, regardless of the ethics involved. This is a matter of survival, and digestion becomes a non-critical operation at the moment.

This of course leaves the stomach on a status-quo basis. It's in the same fix your automatic washing machine would be in if a power rationing board shut off your electricity half way through the job. Possibly it was just time for the machine to pump out the dirty water and take in a supply of fresh water. But now the clothes just lie there and soak while the water grows cold and soap scum gathers on the side of the cylinder. Such treatment is not particularly good for your washing machine but what are you going to do about it? It does no good to argue with a power rationing board. It is foolish to threaten that henceforth you'll take your electricity from somebody else. So you just wait and grimly hope that this sort of thing doesn't happen too often.

Similarly, it does the stomach no particular good to have the digestive process halted in the middle of the job while the gastric juices just rest there and a piece of fried potato settles disconsolately to the bottom of the pot. The stomach doesn't like it. But there again, what's it going to do about it? There's not much it can do, either, except to wait and grimly hope that this sort of thing doesn't happen too often.

The stomach, unfortunately, was designed in a primitive era and the specifications for the human body contain no reference to copper pipes for interior plumbing. The gastric juices must of necessity be powerful so they can dissolve organic matter taken in as food. They must, in fact, be powerful enough to dissolve the very substances that compose the body. And right there was a neat problem for the Master Draftsman to reckon with: If the gastric juices must be powerful enough to digest flesh, what's to prevent a man from completely digesting *himself,* when he settles down to smoke an after-dinner cigar?

To solve this problem, an intricate chemical program was devised whereby the walls of the stomach continually bathe themselves with an acid-resisting mucus, and the system works beautifully except when the stomach gets interrupted.

The stomach was built to stand a certain amount of abuse. It can withstand an occasional shut-down without apparent harm, just as your automatic washing machine can withstand being shut off occasionally before it has had time to rinse itself completely. It is only through prolonged and repeated abuse that trouble develops—with stomachs, or with washing machines.

Primitive man probably knew only one kind of fear—a simple, direct, animal fear. When he casually reached out in the dim light of his cave to pick up a leopardskin sarong and the thing switched its tail and snarled at him, he undoubtedly knew fear. Sudden and powerful fear. But at other times he did not know fear. Panics, depressions, draft boards, internal revenue investigations, bill collectors, and divorce courts hadn't yet been invented. He didn't fear his boss because he had no boss. He didn't fear poverty because he had never known prosperity. He didn't fear hunger for it had been his constant companion.

His simple animal fears ordinarily came equipped with a definite time limit. There is no need to fear a leopard after you have parted his skull with a stone hatchet or beat a strategic retreat. And so with a few temporary interruptions, the digestion of primitive man worked quite smoothly. And he was amazingly free from ulcers.

Modern man has no such primitive advantages. The press and the radio keep him informed of war threats and potential economic upheavals. The insurance companies run full-page ads reminding him of the odds-on possibility that he'll be flat broke and bumming cigarette money from his children at age sixty-five. Well-meaning crusaders vividly portray what's liable to happen to him if he drinks whiskey or smokes cigarettes. The Safety Council keeps him informed of his chances of being smeared all over the highway, while statisticians quote the odds on his keeling over with heart failure or dying with cancer. And when he has a few spare minutes he sits around and searches inwardly for symptoms, and lives in a world of melancholy apprehension.

These fears are different from the simple, direct, animal fears in that they are somewhat abiding and almost eternal. They rise and fall in intensity but few of them completely disappear. The underlying fear of depression or poverty enters into nearly every proposed expenditure of money and provokes unestimated millions of domestic quarrels on the question of extravagance. Minor amounts of fear, guilt, and remorse are often sipped with every cocktail or inhaled with each cigarette, and particularly by the person who has promised himself he'd swear off. The fear of cancer or of heart failure or of tuberculosis may accompany each minor muscular twinge or lesser ailment. Instead of fear coming like a sudden thunder shower and then departing to reveal the clear blue skies of contentment, it remains as an increasing and decreasing drizzle eternally to dampen the spirits.

The digestive process, meanwhile, is in a state of apprehensive confusion governed by subconscious indecision. It stops and starts like a ball player trying to decide to steal second base. Or ultimately, through a spirit of compromise, the subconscious mind permits the stomach to operate on restricted energy rations. Hydrochloric acid swirls about the stomach interior. The mucous membrane, attempting to get along on reduced rations, is not always able to protect the walls. The interrupted action prolongs the acid assault. Actual breaks occur in the membrane lining, permitting the gastric juices to attack the stomach's walls. Small hemorrhages appear—and the stage is completely set for the appearance of an ulcer.

There are more technical details concerning the blushing and the blanching of the stomach walls under emotional stress which would appeal to the medical student. But it should be sufficient here to realize that through simple, natural, logical steps, science has observed the beginning of a pathological ailment as a direct result of an emotional disturbance and there comes the inevitable question: How much good will it do to remove the ulcer through surgery, if the factors which caused the ulcer are not changed? How much good does it do to snip the blossom from the thistle if you do not destroy the roots?

More and more, through half a century, many medical men came to suspect that the roots of a great many pathological ailments are planted somewhere in the subconscious mind, and that the disorder is brought into full bloom by drawing nourishment from disturbed emotions.

The stomach, of course, is only one organ of the elaborate digestive process. And the digestion of food is only one facet of the elaborate problem of survival. Man does not live by bread alone.

We are familiar, all of us, with many another phenomenon brought on by emotions. Embarrassment may bring a rush of blood to the face and neck, indicating that the circulatory system is affected by emotional impact. Fear will affect the sweat glands of the body. Passion will affect the sex organs. An unpleasant sound will produce goose pimples on the skin. Anger will affect the throat and the voice box. The salivary glands may respond to the mere thought of food. And is it any more fantastic or any more fabulous that the recurring and extreme feelings of guilt in the case of Mrs. G. should bring on spasms of the muscles in the walls of the bronchial tubes, a condition otherwise known as an asthma attack?

An attack, when it occurs, is real and physical and pathological. The air passages shrink in size with an accompanying feeling of suffocation. It is preposterous for anyone to suggest that the pain is merely imaginary or that the attack is based upon pretense. It is merely the causative factor that is psychogenic. In exactly the same way, extreme anger may cause a man to kick viciously at a boulder in his pathway. But the pain of his broken toes, a few moments later, is not imaginary.

It may seem odd that the subconscious mind would deliberately order the contraction of the muscles in the walls of the bronchioles when tormented with a feeling of guilt, and thus deliberately bring on misery and suffering. But is it any more odd than the action of a child banging his head against the floor in a temper tantrum? Or a man tearing his hair in a fit of despondency? Or clenching his fists under the strain of anxiety until the nails have dug into the flesh?

It was Winston Churchill who observed that, to him, a change of worries was like a vacation. But the basic idea wasn't original with Mr. Churchill. The subconscious mind operates upon that premise.

There's probably nothing that can get the mind off a vague sense of guilt more efficiently than can an acute attack of asthma.

I imagine most anybody who didn't sleep completely through his hygiene classes in public school, realizes that pain serves a definite purpose in the scheme of our lives. It's a neat and efficient way of warning an individual when he has a hot-foot, and it taught our primitive ancestors how silly it was to leave one foot dangling down from a tree-house perch, where it could be gnawed by a leopard. But pain also serves another common purpose. It is the master switchman of the one-track mind.

The man who beats his head in anguish is not performing a series of nonsensical acts. Even though he is not consciously aware of his motives, there is a cunning strategy behind it. If and when the pain is sufficiently strong to attract the attention of the conscious mind, it will necessarily channel attention away from the cause of his grief. Like Mrs. G.'s attacks of asthma at four o'clock each afternoon, the phenomenon is backed up by remarkable logic seldom recognized by the conscious mind.

There are, of course, many maladies far more subtle than an acute attack of asthma. The human body is an elaborate machine engaged in many tasks. It must wage ceaseless war against the infinite number of germs and bacteria and other microörganisms intent upon its destruction. It must carry food and oxygen to all the living cells, and dispose of the waste. It must reckon with the problems of reproduction for the preservation of the species . . . not to mention the task of remaining socially acceptable and keeping up the payments on the family car.

To achieve this multiplicity of tasks, the body depends upon many different organs; many muscles, fibers, and tissues. And each, in its own way, affects all the others. There is reason to believe that each, in turn, is accountable to the subconscious mind, and that all the factors of body chemistry are influenced by our emotions. Whether it be a feeling of guilt, anger, fear, joy, love, or sorrow, the Chief Operator of the subconscious mind remains faithfully at her post, barking out orders to enable the body to meet the situation at hand, or to build a detour to enable the conscious mind to escape from an intolerable situation.

But there's this much about it: The human body is the net result of all the factors that go into its construction. A little too much acid here, and not quite enough hormones there, can make all the difference in the world—like Grandma's home-made bread when she uses too much yeast and not enough shortening and it turns out to be quite a mess.

It is the premise of psychosomatic medicine that our thoughts and our emotions, our attitudes and our prejudices, all contribute in making us what we are—for richer or for poorer, in sickness and in health. It denies the existence of any discernible dividing line between mental and physical health. It contends that man's mind and his body and his environment stand equally guilty as accessories before the fact, in attempting to place the blame for a great many maladies.

Obviously, the psychosomatic premise must operate under a statute of limitations. It would be a little far-fetched to classify snake bite as a psychosomatic ailment brought on, in part, by the emotional disturbance of the victim. To the best of my knowledge, snakes are elaborately indifferent as to the emotional status of those whom they bite. And yet even here, in specific instances, it may be found that a sudden emotional flare-up was responsible for the victim's relaxing the usual caution which had protected him from snake bite on other occasions.

A commendable effort has been made in recent years to classify certain specific maladies as psychosomatic ailments—ulcers, allergies, high blood pressure, migraine, and so on—while germ-borne maladies are kept apart. But in the final analysis, such arbitrary, sight-unseen, rule-of-thumb classifications can not stand up, for all too often the disturbed emotions must bear their share of guilt in bringing about the lowered resistance which granted the disease its initial foothold. Even such things as highway accidents and industrial accidents follow the psychosomatic pattern in upward of eighty percent of the cases. Either the person responsible for the accident is "accident-prone," or an emotional disturbance has produced a temporary oh-what-the-hell attitude, with a corresponding lapse of ordinary caution—with or without an alcoholic accompaniment.

Under the premise of psychosomatic medicine, we toss our subconscious mind a nasty curve when we keep plaguing it with too many of the wrong kinds of emotions. It does its best to meet the immediate task at hand. But over a period of time the whole institution gets sadly out of balance. The various organs of the body have been so busy meeting emergencies they haven't been able to keep up with their routine chores. The gastric juices have raised hob with the stomach walls. Joints have swollen and stiffened because they haven't been receiving their regular shipments of hormones and other required substances. The blood vessels have lost some of their elasticity because they've been straining too much and haven't been getting the proper diet. And the skin has turned a peculiar color because the liver couldn't find a market for its overproduction and the blood vessels have attempted to carry the surplus to a makeshift epidermic garbage dump.

We've seen the same thing happen on a national scale after the prolonged emergency of war: not enough gasoline to get the workers to their jobs, but such a surplus of potatoes that they have to be dumped by the carload. Public conveyances jammed to the breaking point; inadequate sewer facilities in war-boom communities; a widespread housing shortage and a universal longing for the return of peace.

Such are the problems that men inherited when they decided to live together in an organized society, with a common interest in a common destiny. And similar are the problems that living cells inherited when they decided to throw in their lot together to form a complex, higher type of organism with but futile dreams of immortality.

The case of Mrs. G. with her daily deadline for attacks of asthma was particularly interesting and illustrative, although a trifle disillusioning to those who expect miracles from analysis.

Once Mrs. G. understood the nature of her four o'clock conflicts and her suppressed feelings of guilt, she immediately took steps to eliminate the cause. Before our interviews were completed, she told me that she was making arrangements to go visit her mother whom she hadn't seen in eleven years, and with whom she had corresponded quite infrequently in all that time.

But even before this she had found relief from her almost daily attacks. On the afternoon when she first frankly faced her feelings of guilt toward her mother, she told me in all seriousness:

"It feels good to get this off my chest. I guess I've kept it bottled up inside me too long, and confession is good for the soul. I feel better than I've felt in months, and I give you my word that I won't have an attack at four o'clock this afternoon." And she was right.

Confession and psychoanalysis, of course, are two different things. Confession is a form of verbal regurgitation, to relieve the pressure of the moment. Psychoanalysis, if properly performed, seeks out and eliminates the cause of the pressure.

It is significant that when Mrs. G. finally discussed her early hatred of her mother and her later feelings of profound guilt, she was not amazed in any way. These things, she insisted, she had never honestly faced before. She had never been conscious of their existence. And yet there are degrees of consciousness. A riveter in a boiler factory may tell you in all earnestness that since about the second week on the job he's never noticed the infernal racket of the place. "Honest to John, I don't even hear it." And yet he's not exactly aghast when somebody shouts above the din to remark how noisy it is. Mrs. G.'s lack of awareness of her feelings of guilt apparently was of that type, as is reasonably characteristic of a neurotic reaction. Her emotional conflict was below the level of consciousness. But undoubtedly her consciousness had to hump itself a bit to keep the conflict safely covered.

It would undoubtedly make a more dramatic story if I could blandly explain that Mrs. G. never again had an attack of asthma after our series of interviews. But that, unfortunately, is not the truth. And the very fact that she continued to have attacks at infrequent and irregular intervals makes her case particularly significant in our attempt to understand the psychosomatic premise.

Actually, Mrs. G. had been subject to infrequent and irregular attacks of asthma for a number of years . . . long before she had been asked to sign the affidavit that she was financially unable to contribute toward the support of her mother, and consequently before the result-ing feelings of guilt had ever been experienced.

One could, with logic, argue that the infrequent and irregular at-tacks of asthma were of a different type from those that appeared almost daily at four o'clock in the afternoon. In fact, this is what I honestly believed at the time. The infrequent and irregular attacks I considered to be of pathological origin, no doubt due to some specific allergy. The cause here was real and physical; and if it could be iso-lated it undoubtedly could be weighed upon delicate scales. The attacks that occurred at four o'clock in the afternoon I considered to be intrinsic asthma, caused solely by emotional conflict—a neurotic and synthetic imitation of the genuine attacks. And the fact that the four o'clock attacks disappeared after analysis while the others re-mained, seemed to give credence to the belief.

Still impressed by the apparent logic of this, I offered the case history of Mrs. G. for panel discussion one afternoon in Lima, during the extensive considerations of the psychosomatic premise. Here, I be-lieved, was fairly conclusive evidence that maladies could readily be divided into the two familiar groupings; those of pathological origin and those of psychogenic origin.

The discussion of this case was long and involved and at times highly technical. Nor did all members of the panel agree at all times upon all points. But in the end I believe there was universal agree-ment upon the following:

An abnormal relationship between the child and the mother can so frequently be found in the background of asthma patients as to make the situation reasonably typical. A deep-seated sense of insecurity and an abnormal longing for parental love and parental protection are common. And in all of these, the case of Mrs. G. fitted neatly into the established pattern.

The thoughts, the emotions, the attitudes, the prejudices, and the conflicts of Mrs. G., it was agreed, must be held in some measure responsible for how she acts, not merely at four o'clock in the after-noon but also at all other times.

If it could definitely be established that Mrs. G. was allergic to some particular item, then her allergy was due to the physical and chemical conditioning of her body, in addition to psychological factors. And her thoughts and her emotions would still be jointly accountable for making her the type of person she turned out to be. Her early hatred of her mother, and her intermittent and overwhelming longings for parental love, had left their impressions not merely upon her subconscious mind but also upon the physical development of her body. Her youthful emotions had, in definite measure, affected the chemical recipe from which she was built.

Mrs. G., it was agreed, was the net result of her physical and mental experiences, and of the environment in which these experiences had occurred.

"Isn't there one other thing you're overlooking?" I inquired. "Shouldn't heredity be considered also?"

But the moderator merely shrugged his shoulders, smiled wryly and announced, "We've spent too much time on this discussion already. If we're going to open up the old debates about environment versus heredity, we could still be here six weeks from now."

And with that, the gavel rapped the table and the moderator commenced reading the next paper, and outlining the next topic for panel discussion.

Mrs. G., I imagine, might have been embarrassed if she could have realized how elaborately indifferent these gentlemen could be to all the facts carefully noted in her family Bible.

# 7

*It is indeed a desirable thing to be well descended,
but the glory belongs to our ancestors.*—PLUTARCH

IT IS CONTRARY to our conception of democracy and our faith in
Horatio Alger to take too much stock in heredity. We prefer to believe that all men are created equal, and that any young bootblack
who's willing to help old ladies cross the street can grow up to become President of the First National Bank.

My first contact with the unyielding force of heredity came at a
tender age. I was hardly past my eighth birthday when one day I
found a couple of abandoned wolf cubs out on the prairie. What had
happened to their mother, I never learned. But many of the men
who rode the prairies in those days carried rifles slung from the saddle.
And the shooting of wolves was common.

Actually, my two collie dogs discovered the cubs and approached
them with cautious but excited interest, and they stood back obediently
when I came riding up. The cubs were small and fuzzy and wide-
eyed and somehow pathetic-looking, cowering at the edge of a small
thicket. Whatever instinctive fears they felt must have been counter-
balanced by overwhelming hunger; for although they backed away,
it seemed to me they were eyeing the two collies with something
more than academic interest. And when, after a time, I had succeeded
in capturing them and putting them in my saddle bags, they licked my
fingers with eager anticipation.

Chinaman Charlie was a man of no great sentiment, and it took a
lot of boyish screaming and pleading to keep him from destroying the

pups when I unloaded them at the house that evening. But he finally agreed to let them stay in a box behind the stove until Boss Man— Mr. Burton—could say yes or no.

My father's explicit instructions to Mr. Burton had always been that I should receive no special consideration. But in this case he sat and cracked his knuckles in prolonged indecision.

"Wolves don't make good pets, son," he told me with almost fatherly tolerance. "They're cute little rascals when they're little, but they grow up to be mighty mean."

Chinaman Charlie, all this time, stood over by the kitchen range hissing through his bicuspids and repeating somber advice that nobody had particularly asked for: "Wolf, he no good. You shoot him, bang-bang."

I hated Chinaman Charlie then with an unholy passion, and my boyish tears were no doubt inspired as much by anger as by compassionate sympathy for the poor little wistful-looking cubs.

I promised Mr. Burton, among other things, that I would run away from the farm if he wouldn't let me keep my pups; that I wouldn't take the cattle out to pasture; that I'd probably die if he killed them, and that I'd be much happier dead, anyhow—and I would no doubt get somebody to write a letter to Boston, telling my mother the whole story.

No doubt it was the latter threat that proved the clincher. For in the end, Mr. Burton agreed that the pups could stay temporarily, and that the final decision would be left up to my father at the time of his next visit. But by the time my father arrived at the farm it was too late for the exercise of any veto. The two wolf cubs had become accepted fixtures around the farmhouse. I had named them Nip and Tuck, and they had learned to come when called by name. They were frivolous, happy, and carefree; and they seemed to enjoy the rough play of the farmhands who would crumple their ears and roll them yelping joyously across the porch.

Upon those two pups I lavished all the love of which a small boy is capable. I saved them part of my food from the table. From my wages of ten cents a day, I bought them a pair of fancy collars with polished brass studs. And I spent endless hours teaching them such simple tricks as rolling over and playing dead.

The two collies treated them with an air of practiced indifference, and Chinaman Charlie never once relaxed his mumbled complaints. But aside from these things, Nip and Tuck enjoyed a life of simple pleasures and much affection.

By the end of the first summer their soft coats had grown coarser and their little puppy teeth had approached the point of being dangerous. But still they came when called, and they licked my hands eagerly. And they continued to look upon life as pretty much of a lark.

The first real trouble came in the fall when Chinaman Charlie found his chicken coop littered with feathers, and a couple of old hens missing, and too-satisfied expressions upon the faces of Nip and Tuck. It was purely circumstantial evidence. But without the formality of a trial or any impartial survey of the evidence, he grimly announced that Nip and Tuck would have their skulls parted with a meat cleaver if he ever found them around the house or around the chicken coop again.

As diplomatically as possible, Mr. Burton suggested that I keep them in the barn, and keep them tied. One of the hands, Big Ed, in a rare mood of generosity, strung chicken wire across the end of a vault-like room in the barn that had once been used for storing grain. And here Nip and Tuck made their home, like a couple of caged animals at the zoo, trotting wearily back and forth and obviously yearning for their freedom.

Each day we'd let them out for a romp. And once, contrary to Mr. Burton's orders, I tried to take them along as I drove the cattle out to pasture. But it was a sorry mistake. They would no longer obey my commands and they streaked far across the prairie despite my frantic screams.

Late that night, Nip returned to the farmhouse and Big Ed placed her out in the pen. But it was nearly a week before anyone succeeded in laying hands upon Tuck. He was seen a number of times during that week, but always he lurked just beyond reach. He'd come up and eat from a pan only after we had backed away sufficiently, and he'd shy off each time we attempted to approach. A dozen times, at least, Uncle Charlie and I spread out a lariat near the feed pan and covered it over with dust—and we waited for the time when Tuck would step inside the loop and we could possibly catch him by a leg. But never once did Tuck step into the loop, although several times he impishly pushed the rope away with his paws and gazed in our direction derisively.

Then one evening, shortly after milking time, Tuck trotted into the barn and stood whining outside the pen where Nip was confined. He scratched at the gate and seemed almost impatient to enter. Apparently he had sown his wild oats and was now ready to settle down to the simple life once again.

At the end of their second year Nip and Tuck were nearly grown. But apparently all the loving care that had gone into their upbringing had been in vain. Only rarely would they let me pet them. At other times they cowered, and bared their fangs. Once when Big Ed was a little too bold in pressing his unrequited love, Nip took a nip at him, and left a nasty gash in his forearm. Because of the progressive ugliness of their dispositions, it became increasingly difficult to clean out their pen and increasingly easy to overlook it.

At about this point my father returned to the farm and decided that the experiment had gone far enough. Nip and Tuck, successively, were led out behind the barn, and for each there was one rifle shot— clear and sharp—that echoed through the rafters of the barn and clamped a cold vise about the heart of a small boy up in the hayloft, sobbing uncontrollably.

My father was grim but tolerant. "Some things we have to learn in this life," he told me. "A wolf is born a wolf, and he's always going to be a wolf. And there's nothing you or I can do about it. You can't change the scheme of the world, just to suit your own little plans."

And he took me out to the pen where his prize bull was kept. And he told me why he had paid more than a thousand dollars for that big ornery brute, because he represented the finest stock that was immediately available at the time.

On the way back toward the house he paused beside the small neglected garden plot where Chinaman Charlie had scattered an assortment of seeds. And he knelt down beside a parched and weary-looking cabbage plant.

"What do you suppose would happen," he asked me, "if this poor little plant got enough water, and if we gave it the right amount of fertilizer, and cultivated the soil around it?"

I shook my head without answering. So he answered the question himself: "It would grow, and become full—and healthy. But it would keep right on being a cabbage. No matter how much you cultivate it, and no matter how much you fertilize it, and no matter how much loving care you give it, a cabbage isn't going to grow up to be a rose. And if you're going to cry over such things you're just wasting your tears."

I cried, of course, regardless. But I learned a lesson that had to be learned. And it served me later through all the years of my medical career.

Small boys are not the only ones who are guilty of wishful dreaming. And too many pillows are dampened with wasted tears.

The laws of heredity are sharply defined, and they apply to the human species as surely as they apply to Mendel's variegated peas and to Castle's laboratory mice. Through selective breeding, man has attempted to improve the strain of practically every animal and every plant that has come within his control. But he has somehow refused to believe that the laws of heredity apply to man himself. And he is reluctant to look beyond the bounds of his own epidermis when seeking the cause of any recognized abnormality.

Authentic information as to the patient's family is almost invariably the most difficult information to get, in compiling a case history. The typical patient sets up his defenses immediately and treats the psychiatrist as if he were some kind of gossipy neighbor brazenly asking personal questions. The attitude is generally the same, and readily apparent: "After all, Doc, I came here to find out what's wrong with me; not to find out what was wrong with my grandmother."

There is also a certain natural resentment against any stress of hereditary factors, bolstered by a feeling of futility. By the time the patient reaches the psychiatrist's office, it is far too late in the game for him to go back and pick out a different set of ancestors. "Doc, you're just wasting your time and my time, if you're going to sit here and haggle about heredity. It's too late for either of us to do anything about it." And that, of course, is true.

In a way, the psychiatrist is not unlike the frantic housewife on the morning when the automatic pop-up toaster burns out a bearing and cremates each slice of toast. It's readily apparent that the only real solution would be to repair the toaster. But since that's out of her line, and time is short, and Papa mustn't be late for work—she must content herself with scraping the toast over the sink, and making the best of an unhappy situation.

Psychiatrists, for the most part, must be content with salvage operations. But there is a limit to what they can do.

A complete psychiatric examination can never be content with the examination of one individual. And reluctantly, the psychiatrist must by-pass the beautiful dream of all men being created equal.

There are in the United States, for example, tens of thousands of mental defectives—idiots, imbeciles, and morons. Recent experiments among the amino acids have isolated a remarkable protein food substance known as glutamic acid, and in early tests it offers the cautious promise of aiding mentally defective children in modest degree. But except for this, medical science can offer mental defectives little hope. Society awards them little more than the questionable privilege of reproducing their kind. And they hold their own, at approximately one tenth of one percent of a growing population.

A small percentage of them—usually the more hopeless—are confined to state institutions. They are fed and clothed and jammed in together in a minimum of space, for the need is always greater than the budget. And humanity contributes more generously from the womb than from the wallet.

The idiots and the imbeciles are quiet, for the most part—vacant-eyed and noncomplaining. They ask little of life, and get it: A place to sleep, and food to meet their bodily needs, and a bench to sit on in the sun. From a psychological standpoint, they might almost as well be classified with the vegetable kingdom.

The morons, however, are the mental giants of the group. They come closer to the intellectual average, scoring between forty and seventy in a standard intelligence test, where one hundred represents the average score for the whole population. They generally know which way is up and what comes after Tuesday. They are by far the most numerous of the mental defectives. Thousands of them hold down routine jobs, are self-supporting, and highly prolific. They are not mentally ill, in the usual sense. They have lost no mental power; they simply never had too much in the first place. They'll visit the obstetrician far more often than they'll visit the psychiatrist. If they constitute a problem, it is a social problem and not primarily a psychiatric problem.

By selection, and by the process of elimination, they frequently marry pretty close to type. And barring highly conspicuous exceptions, their descendants may stray not too far from their footsteps. If mental deficiency were as apparent to the naked eye as is the color of the skin —then the morons would constitute a distinctive and ever-increasing race with limited interracial marriages.

Various extensive studies, however, indicate that the moron is a reasonably successful animal in the midst of modern environment. He is productive, prolific, and easily entertained. He earns more money than the average for the whole population. He is emotionally more stable than his highly intelligent cousin, and less susceptible to a host of psychosomatic ailments. He may be a dependable worker, and a reasonably pleasant type of neighbor. And it is pertinent to note that the highly successful Prussian war lords considered him the very finest type of soldier, not only in the field but in certain elementary positions of command.

There has been a certain amount of backsliding in recent years among prominent psychologists, and a growing reluctance to term an individual a moron upon the basis of his mental ability alone. Largely under the influence of the British Mental Deficiency Committee, there has come a tendency to apply the term only to those persons in the forty-to-seventy I.Q. bracket who can't readily adjust to the demands of their environment and who require special care, supervision, or control. So far, it has served to confuse rather than to clarify, and represents but one more example of how a given word in our language may be subject to changing definitions.

The change in this case is due, no doubt, to the ridicule and the contempt that the general public applies to the term, resulting, at least in part, from the flood of Little Moron stories that swept the Western world and found their way into the anthologies of humor.

But no matter what we call them, there remain the tens of thousands of persons in this country who can't turn in a passing grade in an intelligence test but who remain good citizens, and who make good workers, good neighbors, good soldiers and good sailors. The man with a high I.Q. enjoys certain distinct advantages when he's reading and writing and handling abstractions. But conceivably, he might be the first to drown in a shipwreck.

The psychological backsliding will undoubtedly prove to be beneficial in the long run, even though it creates a certain amount of confusion in the process. Eventually it will reflect itself in the general public attitude. In this country we've turned thumbs down on titles of nobility, and we rebel against class distinction. But we've tried hard to build up a sort of mental aristocracy. We've taken for granted that the man with a high I.Q. is better equipped for life than is the man with a moderately low I.Q. And it isn't necessarily so.

The man with a healthy body and a happy disposition is probably better prepared for a good life on this earth, than is the man who lacks these things but has a broad splash of intellectual genius. And he'll produce more, and healthier, and happier children—and plant fewer seeds of neurosis.

Naturally, the person who is tone deaf might be foolish to try to find a career on the concert stage. And the man who hits below par on his I.Q. test might be foolish to try to find a career in science and invention, or in some other field dependent upon intellectual achievement. But our civilization could not endure if it had a population made up entirely of scientists and inventors.

A number of years ago a distraught mother brought her fifteen-year-old son to my office and explained that he seemed a little "slow" in school. He was then in the fifth grade.

"He's a good boy," she told me tearfully. "He's never caused me a minute's trouble, but he just can't learn. I want you to do whatever you can for him. I've saved up nearly four thousand dollars and I'm willing to spend every cent of it to get him fixed up."

The son, it developed, had the mentality of an average eight-year-old. School reports indicated that he had been passed along from the first to the fifth grade over a period of nine years, largely because of his size. He had never satisfactorily completed the work of any single grade even though he'd spent two years in each, through the fourth. The reports indicated that he had never been involved in any trouble at school. His teachers described him as kind, gentle, and quite well liked by the other children. But aside from that, he mostly just sat.

I explained to the mother, then, that there was nothing I could do for her son. She was tearful and almost bitter. But as best I could, I attempted to explain to her that she had no great cause for grief. The boy was in good health and seemed emotionally stable. He merely lacked any talents for academic learning, just as some people lack any talent for art, or for music, or for doing things with their hands.

Since it seemed entirely futile to keep the boy in school, I suggested that an effort be made to find some routine type of work that he could do and enjoy. He started mowing lawns and gradually built up a regular route as a gardener. With a slight assist from changing economic conditions he wound up several years later earning a very adequate living. At age twenty-five, ten years after the visit to my office, I learned that he was married and the father of four children. He was buying his own home in an older neighborhood, owned his own gardening truck and equipment, and seemed quite comfortably contented.

At that time he called at my office and complained of pains in his back and hips.

"Who's your regular doctor?" I inquired. "What makes you think you need psychiatric help?" But he merely shrugged in embarrassed confusion.

"I got no regular doctor. My wife, she wanted me to go to old Doc Townsend, but he's a woman's doctor." He twisted uncomfortably on his chair, and then blurted out: "Hell, you're the only doctor I ever been to. I figured if you couldn't fix me up, you could maybe tell me who to go to."

And that statement, in itself, was eloquent testimony of a successful life in a modern society. And particularly in contrast to the thousands of neurotic individuals of relatively high intelligence who eternally haunt the waiting rooms of medical men from coast to coast.

Further proof could possibly be found in his willing acceptance of my diagnosis of the ailment as "backache," and the ready agreement to accept such a simple treatment as heat and massage of the home-applied variety . . . following which he reported substantial improvement in very short time. A more intelligent, better-educated, and more prosperous patient with identical symptoms would perhaps require a diagnosis as "fibrositis," which carries a more dignified ring and substantiates a more impressive claim to temporary invalidism.

There is little doubt that nervous tension brings muscular tension, and that these two, working hand-in-hand, are substantial contributors to our modern epidemic of backache symptoms. In the armed forces, particularly, the "convenient backache" is the ever-ready complaint of the so-called goldbrick. And in civilian life it's apt to show up at harvest time, canning time, plowing time . . . or any other time to prevent an individual from going ahead with the job that he or she didn't particularly want to tackle in the first place.

With some, it is no doubt a convenient pretense. But with the vast majority there can be little doubt that the pain is real, intensified by emotional dread which erupts into neuro-muscular tensions. And the purpose of the simple massage is twofold: It relaxes the muscles, and it also soothes the emotions—just as petting the family cat may bring purring contentment.

Grandpa no doubt got his money's worth from his proverbial bottle of liniment, and the sympathetic caress of Grandma's capable fingers across his aching back, while she inquired with honest concern, "Does that feel better, now?" And certain advantages rest today with those whose heredity and training haven't ruled out the capacity for benefit from such simple therapy.

Just recently a young lady of above-average intelligence called upon me for advice.

"I have an aunt and two cousins who are in mental institutions," she told me bluntly. "My husband was recently released from the psycho ward of a Veterans Administration hospital, although there is no record of insanity elsewhere in his family. We want to know whether it's safe for us to have children. What do you think?"

"Do you want children?" I asked.

"I wouldn't be here if we didn't," she explained simply. "We want children more than we want anything else in the world. But we wouldn't want to bring a child into the world if he's going to be—well—not all right, mentally."

Her husband, it developed, had gone through World War II, serving much of the time as a naval gunner on merchant ships, and often on ships carrying munitions. Once he'd been aboard a ship that was torpedoed at sea, and he'd spent eleven days in a life raft. But not until after he'd returned to civilian life had he shown any signs of abnormality. Then, quite suddenly, he'd started acting strangely, and he'd been taken to the hospital after he'd been found wandering aimlessly down the highway, unable to explain who he was or where he was going. He'd been in the hospital for several months, and she understood that he had received shock treatments.

The aunt and the two cousins confined to mental institutions, I learned, had manic depressive psychoses. And it became my sad duty to explain to the young lady that of all the functional psychoses, the manic depressive states seem most closely to follow a pattern of heredity. And, unfortunately, there's some evidence that the disorders are more frequently transmitted through the female side of the family than through the male side.

So far as the husband was concerned, in view of his hectic wartime experiences and the fact that there was no record of abnormality elsewhere in the family, it seemed just a little like bending over backward, I explained, to fear hereditary tainting from that source.

"In other words," the young lady said thoughtfully, "if we went ahead and had a family, and the children turned out not quite right, it would probably come from my side of the family. That's a terrible thing to have to face."

"Mrs. X.," I told her, "that's something that every prospective parent has to face. I don't know of any mental or physical abnormalities in my family or in my wife's family, as far back as the records can be checked. And yet before each of our children was born, I spent weeks chewing my fingernails and wondering if they'd be all right. If thinking bad thoughts had any influence, they'd have all been Mongoloid idiots with clubfeet."

She smiled mechanically, and then attempted to brush aside all such trivia with another blunt question:

"What's your advice then, Doctor? Do you think we should go ahead and have children, or not?"

"You want a simple answer, yes or no?" I asked.

She nodded.

"Then I'm awfully sorry," I told her. "You've brought your question to the wrong person. After all, I've had but a scant fifty years to study this business. Possibly with ten or twenty times that amount of experience, I'd commence to approach the point where I could give yes or no answers to such questions."

She looked a little startled, began to speak, then pressed her lips tightly together and waited for me to continue, or to make the first motion toward the door.

"There are no written guarantees that ever come with parenthood," I told her. "I'd be very happy to discuss with you what little I've been able to learn about hereditary factors in mental disorders. But when it comes to a final decision as to whether you should have children, I'm afraid that's a question that you and your husband will have to decide. The best I can possibly do is to quote the approximate odds, but you'll have to place your own bets, and be prepared to stand behind them."

She nodded. "I understand that. What are the odds?"

So I explained to her that in reality we know very little about hereditary factors in relationship to mental abnormality. Statisticians tell us that approximately fifty to sixty percent of the schizophrenics can point to mental illness elsewhere in the family. But viewing the same figures from the opposite angle, it means that from forty to fifty percent of the cases seem to pop up just from spontaneous combustion, in a family that has no record of mental illness.

The manic depressive psychoses seem to span down through successive generations to a greater extent than would seem entirely sporting, if governed solely by the laws of chance. Certain types of feeble-mindedness are so directly inherited as to meet the general Mendelian laws.

But aside from these things, we are largely groping in the dark. Many of our specific mental ailments appear to be peculiar to the human species. Experiments with white mice or sunflower seeds are therefore of little avail. The human family, with its long span of time between generations, does not lend itself readily to laboratory experiment, and studies that must span the centuries are a bit discouraging when they must stretch out into the future rather than being summarized from the past.

There are, unfortunately, surprisingly few reliable records up to the past half century, for accurate methods of measurement and of classification were extremely limited.

Family histories, with a few notable exceptions, were composed of a strange hodge-podge of speculation, hearsay, and family gossip. Great-Great-Grandpapa Scroggins may have been considered a little "queer," and this fact may be dutifully noted in the family Bible. But it is practically impossible at this late date to determine whether he was judged queer because he was a victim of paranoia, or whether the rest of the family decided he was queer because he suddenly determined to vote the Democratic ticket. There can be no reliable decisions reached from the study of unreliable facts.

A reliable study of heredity should perhaps concern a few families through a great many generations, rather than following a great many families through a comparatively few generations. Of necessity, our studies have been broad but not deep. And we are perhaps not unlike the well digger who strikes impenetrable rock, and proceeds to dig a hole that is sixty feet across, and four feet deep. It is a good way to work off surplus energy, but not particularly apt to strike water.

And yet even at this early date, a few great promises are commencing to appear through a thin and strange assortment of apparently contradictory facts. Just as a running stream is said to purify itself as it flows along, so, apparently, does the human strain purify itself as it progresses through the successive generations and on through the centuries. Heredity, rather than being a means of spreading the mental contamination to encompass the entire species, may be our one real hope of gradually blotting up the abnormalities as recessive characteristics.

"Do you think it would be reasonably safe for us to have children, then?" the young lady in my office asked eagerly. But I merely returned the serve.

"The important question is: Do you think it would be worth the gamble? Do you want children enough so that you'd risk the long-odds chance of getting a child who's not entirely normal? Would you be prepared to love him and care for him, regardless?"

Her eyes were moist when she answered: "If he was my child—our child—our very own—I'd love him, no matter what. I'd take care of him and I'd love him . . . even if he turned out to be a Mongoloid idiot with clubfeet, like you said." She smiled jauntily, but a single tear slid down her cheek.

"An enviable heredity is a wonderful thing," I told her. "If we wanted really to practice selective breeding, we could undoubtedly improve the strain of the human herd. But there's every logical reason to believe that the vast majority of the world's misfits are made, not born."

It is particularly difficult, I have discovered on occasional trips to Las Vegas, to predict accurately just what combination of cherries, prunes, bars, lemons, or other symbols will show up on the three spinning wheels of a slot machine.

It is infinitely more difficult to predict just what combination of characteristics will show up when the hundreds of thousands of genes within the male and female germ cells get together at the moment of conception. It is almost as if one had tripped the handle of a giant slot machine, to send hundreds of thousands of wheels spinning. Round and round they go, and where they'll stop nobody knows. The possible combinations are almost infinite in number. So much so, that in all the centuries of recorded history, there's no evidence that the same combination has appeared twice, to produce two identical individuals. (Identical twins don't count, for they develop from the same germ cells, and constitute a doubling up of the bet, on a single spin of the wheels.)

But once the combination is determined—once the genes have paired off, organized their new corporation, elected their officers and started into business, then certain things are determined, including the color of the eyes and the color of the hair, and the potential stature—both mental and physical. Whether the individual will ever reach that potential, or find it satisfying, is something else again.

The influence of environment begins not at the moment of birth, but at the moment of conception. The mother's diet, activity, physical structure, and so on, all commence to influence the new organism, and to help determine whether it will achieve its potential.

It is a fascinating form of gambling, and potential parenthood is always based upon a certain calculated risk. But there's every reason to believe that heredity deals with us far more kindly than do the Las Vegas slot machines.

My father was correct, of course, years ago: With all the loving care it is possible to give it, a cabbage will never grow up to be a rose. But he could have added that without a reasonable amount of intelligent care, the finest cabbage seed in all the world won't grow up to be even a good cabbage. And there's the saddest part of the whole sad business.

# 8

*The true test of civilization is, not the census, nor the size of cities, nor the crops, but the kind of man that the country turns out.*—EMERSON

MEDICAL SCIENCE FOR many years has attempted to trace a convenient dividing line between the communicable and the noncommunicable ailments of mankind. But there arises a suspicion that it is a futile effort based upon a false premise. Such germ-free and supposedly noncommunicable maladies as automobile accidents, hysteria, suicides, and doing imitations of Al Jolson, all may break out in epidemic proportions just the same as mumps or measles or scarlet fever.

Men, collectively, help to shape the environment in which they live. And the environment, in turn, helps to determine what kind of men the country will produce. By banding together to preserve their independence, men build also a great bond of interdependence. Their habits, attitudes, fads, foibles, and philosophies tend to rub off on one another.

During the days of World War II, we were given a unique opportunity to study the kind of men our country is producing in modern times. And it was not altogether an inspiring revelation. More than four and a half million men were rejected at the induction centers of the nation. And nearly forty percent of these were rejected because of some type of personality disorder—certainly not a germ-borne ailment.

During the turbulent days of that war, it became my peculiar duty to serve as psychiatric examiner at the military induction center in

Los Angeles—a task that might be compared with an attempt to judge the quality of the rivets in a jet plane as it zips past at seven hundred miles an hour.

A complete psychiatric examination cannot be achieved in minutes or in hours. It may require days, if one is to start right from scratch and attempt to gather the information for an adequate case history. And yet the war could possibly have been lost while training camps still awaited the arrival of their first recruits, if we had taken time for a methodical examination of each man who showed up at the induction center.

In actual practice, I sat at a desk and interviewed the men as they meandered up in their birthday suits; raw recruits from the city's East side—zoot-suiters without their suits, and with their long hair strangely incongruous against the unpadded form of their nakedness. College men in the prime of life. Young fathers, often self-conscious. Now and then a famous star from the Hollywood movie colony, clad in no more dignity or glamor than the dishwasher from a Main Street hash-house. Men of every race and creed, and from all walks of life, responding voluntarily to the call of duty or responding to Uncle Sam's meaningful tap upon the shoulder.

And because of the speed of the assembly-line procedure, a typical interview consisted of little more than an oral greeting, a few casual questions about the man's status in civilian life, and then a sideward nod of the head that could be interpreted to mean "You're in the Army now."

And now and then as the men moved on, I could hear a puzzled question near the door. "What in the hell was that all about?" It must have been a disillusioning experience for those who had pictured a psychiatrist as a modern Svengali with thick-lens glasses, who'd invite them onto his couch and explain the hidden significance of last night's dreams. They'd found merely a tired old man with a few trite questions. And that was all.

I heard one recruit in the hallway express what must have been the reaction of many: "God Almighty! I've had a more complete examination when I've tried to buy a pound of butter at the grocery store!"

And yet, I imagine, many of them would have been amazed if they could have understood how efficient was this screening process, all things considered. It is not all poetic nonsense that the eyes are the mirror of the soul.

A friend of mine, a prominent pediatrician in Hollywood who has an exceptionally large practice, once told me that he could give an entirely adequate routine examination of an infant in something less than thirty seconds—by merely looking at the eyes and feeling of the abdomen.

"But no mother would be satisfied with that," he told me, smiling wearily. "She's probably gone to a lot of trouble to bring the child to the office, and she expects me to give it the works." And so he depresses the tongue and examines the throat, makes the traditional passes with his stethoscope, peers into the ears and inspects the hands and feet, and has his nurse arrange for very business-like checking of height and weight.

"Possibly once in a thousand times I find something I didn't expect to find," he told me. "But when you've examined as many babies as I have in my lifetime, you can tell a whale of a lot at a glance."

And during my days at the induction center, I felt that I could do a reasonably adequate job of detecting the neurotics and the psychotics and the mental defectives with little more than a quick glance and a conversation that seldom lasted three minutes, at most—unless those three minutes produced some evidence of abnormality.

Questions asked were routine and varied: How old are you? Where were you born? Do you want to be in the Army? How often do you go to church? How did you get along in school? But always during an interview I attempted to present at least one question that the young man hardly expected, and which he could not answer without a momentary pause and thoughtful consideration, or a response of surprise and indecision. Sometimes it was purely a nonsensical question: Why is a battleship, if it doesn't sink?

Undoubtedly there was many a young man who went dubiously

on his way, convinced that the old boy at the desk was the one who really should see a psychiatrist. But in that off-guarded moment of confusion and uncertainty, with his eyes suddenly quizzical and his eyebrows arched, and a wrinkle spread across his forehead, he had stood openly revealed. He hadn't been sure if he'd heard correctly. He hadn't known whether to laugh. He'd been so busy trying to make sense out of a nonsensical question that he'd forgotten, momentarily, to wear the practiced mask of anonymity. And in that moment his thought processes had been as easy to trace as is the course of a mole across a golf green.

Thinking may not be a muscular process, but it produces muscular reaction as a by-product. Just as a normal person unconsciously moves the strategic muscles of the oral cavity when reading silently—and just as the deaf mute makes motions with his fingers as he reads—so does the person who is thinking, trace the pattern of his thoughts in the tensing of facial muscles.

By intensive training an individual may learn to make no visible movement of tongue or lips in silent reading. He strives to not pronounce each word, physically. And yet with delicate measuring instruments, the slight tensing of these muscles can be detected in the most highly trained of silent readers. Yes, and the deaf mute who has learned to speak sign language will continue to tense the muscles of his fingers as he reads, no matter how he strives not to do so.

By intensive training an individual may learn to mask his thoughts and emotions. He may pride himself on being a perfect poker face. But still the tensing of the strategic muscles goes on, even though their movements have become invisible to the naked eye.

The thoughts we think and the emotions we experience determine the amount of exercise these various muscles will receive, and the amount of exercise they receive determines, in turn, how they will develop. And just as the biceps of a blacksmith may differ from those of a bookkeeper, so does the facial expression of a genius differ from that of a moron; and so does the expression of an emotionally stable person differ from that of a psychotic. To me, this is not fantastic. It would be fantastic if it were otherwise.

By the time a man has achieved his growth, his character is etched indelibly upon his face. It shows in every line about the eyes, and in the expression of the eyes themselves. But more particularly, it shows about the mouth and lips which are more closely associated with the process of speech. It shows in the chin, and in the set of the jaws.

There can be little doubt that grave injustices are done in this world when a man with a homely face is shunned as the "criminal type," and when an attractive girl is automatically classified as "beautiful but dumb." It is a convenient and a commendable theory that a man's appearance offers no index to his nature. But unfortunately, it isn't true.

It is quite unlikely that the untrained observer will ever be much shucks at judging character by the appearance of a man's face; just as it is quite unlikely that the untrained observer will ever be able to sit down and read a tablet written in Egyptian hieroglyphics. A certain amount of training seems almost essential.

I would be entirely untruthful if I intimated that my hasty appraisal of the men passing before me at the induction center was not influenced greatly by general appearance. And I realize that I differ from many of my colleagues in placing such emphasis on facial expression.

The men passing before me represented every possible shade of mental stature from imbecile to genius. They represented all gradations from normal specimens to advanced psychotics. And it would be foolish to imply that I, or anyone else, could unerringly detect all of the incipient or borderline cases with such cursory examination.

The fact that some forty-three percent of medical discharges from the services, after induction, were neuropsychiatric cases offers eloquent testimony that we didn't screen out all of the potential cases.

In a way, we who served as psychiatric examiners at the induction centers were little different from the thousands of others serving as graders and sorters of all kinds and types of materials, working at top speed in the war plants of the nation.

There were airplane motors that conked out under the strain and abuse of battle conditions. There were guns that jammed and ships that broke in two under enemy attack. And yet these things are almost inevitable when the stresses and strains which become unavoidable, surpass the tensile strength of the materials involved. And the same is true in a human equation. The graders and the sorters of men and of materials must merely do the best they can under a particular circumstance, knowing that all things have their respective breaking points.

At the opening of the medical conference in Lima, Peru, in 1946, I was challenged to prove my contention that the hasty psychiatric examinations in the United States induction centers had been reasonably reliable under the circumstances. And particularly I was challenged on my statement that a trained observer could judge much by facial expression and appearance. Delegates to the conference were not all psychiatrists. There were physicians and surgeons, specialists in every branch of medicine, from all parts of the world. And I had no reason to suppose they were particularly prejudiced in my favor. Psychiatry is still a Johnny-come-lately in the medical field.

For purposes of demonstration, then, between twenty-five and thirty persons were placed on the stage. Sheets were employed as improvised screens, so that I could see nothing but the individual's head. And it was my task, before the audience, to attempt classification. Those on the stage had been carefully selected to represented a gamut of types, from intellectuals to mental defectives, and from men of unquestioned integrity to convicted habitual criminals borrowed from local jails, for the duration of the demonstration.

It was agreed at the outset that I was to attempt to select those who might be good material for military service, and to weed out those whose mental or emotional make-up might prove to be a liability rather than an asset to a military organization.

Some I selected and some I rejected, without a word being spoken. Among those selected, I learned later, was an admiral in the United States Navy. And among those rejected was a convicted rapist with a long criminal record.

With others, I found it necessary to ask questions. But they were in all cases casual or irrelevant questions similar to those asked at the induction center. They were asked, not to gain information as to the individual's background, but rather to observe reaction and response, the tone of voice, the facial expression—the comprehension or the lack of comprehension mirrored in the eyes.

During the time allotted for the demonstration, I classified twenty-odd persons. The procedure was slowed down by frequent questions from the floor:

"Doctor, you rejected that last man as being unfit for military service. What is there about his appearance that guides your judgment?"

To the best of my ability, I attempted to answer such questions. But it is a difficult situation, comparable to asking a professional coffee taster to please explain why he likes sample "A" better than sample "B." The questions and answers, I'm afraid, served little purpose except to confuse everybody and slow down the process.

However, the committee that arranged and judged the demonstration agreed that I had classified correctly in all cases but one. The single exception was a Methodist minister, whom I'd rejected as not likely military material. He was a fine man, I learned later. Highly respected. I offered him my personal apologies which he accepted graciously; and with an average above ninety-five percent I could afford to be magnanimous about it.

There was, of course, one definite advantage to me on that afternoon in Lima. The committee on arrangements had tackled its assignment with an eye toward showmanship, to present the gamut of types, from admirals to alcoholics. Seldom in a lifetime would you find such a conglomerate assortment of human samples on a single stage. And my assignment would have been infinitely more difficult if the committee had chosen thirty persons at random, from the street.

At the induction center in Los Angeles there naturally was no such advantage in extremes, and there were many criticisms of the type of examination offered. But a good many of the criticisms were inspired more in jest than in earnest. There were infinite gags and wisecracks and the resulting nervous laughter, rippling up and down the line of potential recruits.

"I'll tell you how it is, Mac: They got these two doctors standing there, and you pass between 'em. One looks in your left ear and the other looks in your right ear, and if they can't see each other, you're in the Army."

There were many variations of this and other basic gags. But almost without exception, the men facing examination spoke banteringly of their cherished dreams to win a 4-F classification. And almost without exception, also, the men who'd been singled out of the moving line for possible rejection were the most morose of the lot.

There was little good-natured bantering here, and small evidence of relief. A few of them, of course, were learning of physical infirmities for the first time and this situation obviously offered a sobering effect. But others had known all along of their disability, had come to the center fully expecting to be rejected. And they were equally morose.

I remember one young man in particular because I had often listened to him on the radio, although I had nothing to do with his rejection. He'd come to the induction center armed with letters from several physicians and affidavits from employers and civic leaders. The letters pointed out that he was physically unfit for military service because of a chronic liver condition, and the affidavits grimly pointed out that morale on the home front would practically collapse if the radio broadcasting industry lost the services of this promising young star.

At the time when I first met him, he'd already been singled out for rejection, but he was arguing vehemently against it.

"So maybe I do have a small spot on my liver," he protested. "Chances are you wouldn't even have found it, if I hadn't brought those letters with me. And I'll tell you what I'll do: I'll put up five hundred bucks cash, and if I can't outhike nine-tenths of the guys you've just passed, and if I can't live as well as any of 'em on Army food, you can keep the five hundred bucks and give it to the U.S.O."

His arguments, of course, were entirely futile. But I have no doubt that they were sincere at the time.

"These young punks aren't consistent," a weary medical examiner told me later. "They come armed to the teeth with all kinds of arguments why they should be deferred; and then when you find one who's not physically fit, he rares back on his haunches and wants to spend the rest of the day arguing the point." He shook his head sadly and wandered back to his post of duty.

But that, in reality, is a basic trait of human nature, and it plays a conspicuous part in making us what we are—at induction centers, and elsewhere. Standing in line, the young man finds identification with those ahead of him and those behind him. He is part of the crowd; a member of the mob. He's on the team, momentarily, and he shares a common lot with his fellow men. And even though it may mean rising for reveille and eventually facing enemy bullets in a remote foxhole, he is reluctant at the moment to break away, and to be different from the rest.

This yearning to "belong" is part of the plot in every normal individual's life story. It is the basic lure of the sorority or the fraternity. It does more to boost the enrollment of service clubs than all of the membership drives combined. It is the mysterious mortar used by dictators, labor leaders, football coaches, recruiting sergeants, successful politicians, and organizers of company bowling teams. It is the miracle-adhesive of the family, the city, and the state. It is the stuff that promotes such sudden fads as miniature golf, Chinese checkers, jigsaw puzzles, and Knock-Knock-Who's-There? It's the I-want-to-go-where-you-go-and-do-what-you-do instinct of the species.

Man, by nature, is a social animal. He finds security in the center of the herd. He instinctively opposes the idea that his destiny is his own personal responsibility. He buys insurance and he plans programs of social security. He organizes governments, and he goes beyond that to organize governments into leagues. He gropes eternally for that greater strength which comes with greater numbers, and for that fuller confidence which comes through an alliance with others. Fear dwindles in ratio to the increasing size of the mob.

At home or office, a man may rebel at the idea of being singled out for shipment abroad to help fight a war. But at the induction center, plopped down in the midst of men being pushed through for military service, he may rebel once again at the idea of being singled out—this time for rejection.

And the weary medical examiner obviously was wrong. Even though a man may reverse his position, or his attitude toward induction, he is nothing if not consistent. He wants to be on the team. And his ideas may change from day to day or from hour to hour, depending upon which team he's considering at the moment.

Men need and seek assurance in the midst of an unpredictable world, drawing courage from one another, and preferring to think of the hazards of the future in terms of the plural pronoun. Fears live and grow in isolation, and they find fertile soil in the mind of the individual who feels he does not "belong."

Generally speaking, so long as the individual strives to find security in the center of the herd (and almost regardless of the herd he happens to choose) he may be considered reasonably normal. When, for one reason or another, he commences to withdraw from the group—when he no longer seeks social approval or human acceptance, but seeks his satisfactions in isolation and in solo flights of imagination and day-dreaming—he is embarked upon the road to abnormality.

But there are hazards as well as advantages to this let's-all-stick-together-and-live-the-same-kind-of-life-and-think-the-same-kind-of-thoughts philosophy. Freedom from fear is a noble thing to discuss in generalized terms. But when the human animal finds freedom from fear in the midst of an organized or disorganized mob, the results are not always beneficial to the progress of civilization.

A dozen teen-agers, piled into an ancient jalopy cruising down the street, find a certain freedom from fear because of the security in numbers. With sudden hilarious abandon, they may commence shouting taunts and insults at pedestrians and show a peculiar disregard for social inhibitions. The driver of the jalopy, captured by the mood of the moment, may drive in erratic fashion. And all twelve of the youngsters, jammed in together, may behave in a manner that none would consider or even condone as a single isolated individual.

In a larger sense, the same thing can happen to an entire nation, fanned by the organizing genius of a dictator and by the carefully couched propaganda of press agents who know the basic tenets of mob psychology. War hysteria, lynchings, riots, revolutions, and a host of similar things can spring from man's yearnings to "belong."

In a less dramatic way, a highly regimented type of social life and a remarkably standardized environment may spring from the universal effort to "keep up with the Joneses." With the press, and radio and television all acting as a leveling influence, backed up by such things as uniform laws, graduated income taxes, standardized rules of etiquette, night school classes in home management, and so on, we strive to give our youngsters the same kind of meals and the same kind of vitamin pills and the same kind of training within the home and within the school. And these things, in a broad way, determine what kind of men the nation will produce.

Every thought, every prejudice, every mood or whim or emotion is in some measure communicable.

Heredity, alone, could not explain the more than four and a half million young men, supposedly in the prime of life, who had to be rejected at the induction centers during World War II, because they couldn't meet the most elementary requirements for physical, mental, and emotional health. And a nation determined to do something about it, must do more than merely enrich its flour, and frantically produce more bathtubs and more vitamin pills. It must consider also its way of life, and inquire, thoughtfully, "What, if anything, is wrong with the way we raise our children?"

Among the many persons I have been called upon to examine during more than half a century, there are two case histories that are remarkably similar in many respects, but they illustrate the sharp division between a normal desire to "belong," and an abnormal desire to withdraw from human contact and social approval.

Leon Z. and Robert O. had both served time on several occasions in penal institutions. There was no significant difference in their records on the police blotters. They were both approximately the same age, twenty-four and twenty-seven, respectively. They were both of average intelligence, had both been raised in the same general section of the

city and at one time both had attended the same school, although I
have no record that they knew each other.

Each, in turn, had graduated from auto theft to such things as
armed robbery, and assault with a deadly weapon. Each had come
from an unwholesome home environment, and each had a negative
family history so far as known mental disorders were concerned.

It became my duty to examine both of these boys. And while the
records appeared strikingly similar on the surface, the motives behind
their misdeeds proved exactly opposite.

Leon Z., a youngster of foreign birth and of small stature, raised
most of his life in poverty, had tackled his life of crime in a desperate
attempt to win social approval. Not the approval of the city's best
citizens, it's true—but the approval of the only society he really knew.
He couldn't be the biggest, or best-dressed youngster in his block. He
lacked the aptitude to be the best baseball player or the best marbles
player. His swarthy skin was heavily pockmarked, so he couldn't be
the best-looking boy. But he discovered at an early age that he could
gain a certain amount of awed respect by being the toughest boy in the
neighborhood. His willingness to risk his neck and to risk his freedom had been the price of his initiation into a youthful gang of
hoodlums. And he had paid it willingly. He had wanted to "belong."

Earlier attempts at youthful rehabilitation in corrective institutions
had been of no avail, for they had never offered him the one thing he
demanded—the opportunity to be accepted as a member of a group,
upon his release from the institution. Leon Z. could not find satisfaction as a lone wolf, and in that he was reasonably normal.

Physically, Robert O. was considerably larger. His skin was fair and
smooth, his hair blond and his features delicate. Except for a lack of
masculine ruggedness and a not particularly pleasing expression, he
might almost have been considered good-looking. He, too, had been
raised in comparative poverty, with a mother of questionable morals
and a father who was alternately a raging lion when intoxicated and a
contrite and gentle lamb when sober. But there was no indication that
Robert O. had been inspired by any desire for social approval. In his
own honest words: "I just don't give a damn about people." He com-

mitted his crimes for reasons entirely mercenary, and he spent his profits at houses of prostitution.

His was one of the more sordid stories of sadism and perversion. Even as a child, he told me, he used to sneak downstairs on nights when his father came home drunk, and he'd derive a certain excited satisfaction from watching his father mercilessly beat his own mother. He'd lived through an era of self-abuse and grotesque daydreams, and then had embarked upon his own career of inflicting torture and indulging his peculiar satisfactions in sadism.

He had no desire to "belong." He was a lone wolf socially, professionally, and emotionally—a psychopathic and sadistic pervert yearning to see eyes wide with fear and terror, and faces twisted with pain, but apparently with no desire to see eyes filled with admiration or acceptance.

Even after all these years, I find myself with a strong desire to go home and take a nice clean bath, after an interview with somebody like Robert O. But the moral shock departed years ago, and there's little room for self-righteousness or contempt.

Robert O. was merely the victim of a communicable disease contracted, no doubt, in the days of his childhood. He was no more responsible for being what he was, than would be a victim of leprosy.

To the best of my knowledge, society failed completely in its efforts toward rehabilitation of both these boys in the years that followed— if one is generously to assume that there was any honest effort toward rehabilitation.

Leon Z. is in a state penitentiary at the present time. He is possibly counting the days until completion of his current sentence, but it is little more than the futile waste of simple mathematics unless some method is devised whereby he can gain respect and sympathy and the full rights of membership in society, upon his release. And in his particular case it is perhaps too late for he may be already irrevocably committed to the course he chose through desperation, many years ago.

Robert O. is "at liberty," having completed his last sentence and having so far avoided his next potential confinement. But it is a peculiar kind of "liberty," for he is a registered pervert and an "ex-con." He is periodically questioned, frisked, and kept under surveillance. He is an automatic suspect for any crime in his particular category. He is reasonably typical of tens of thousands of perverted and psychopathic individuals who helped to swell the total of 1,825,000 young American men screened out at the induction centers during World War II, because of personality disorders.

He is the unfortunate by-product of a nation that spends billions for soap and toothpaste and antiseptics of all kinds, and gives too little thought to social sanitation.

# 9

*What mean ye, fellow citizens, that ye turn every stone
to scrape wealth together, and take so little care of your
children, to whom ye must one day relinquish all?*

—SOCRATES

IT IS DIFFICULT, today, to stand and watch the flowing stream of traffic
on a city's busy streets, and to realize that just a comparatively short
time ago children came scampering excitedly out of houses to watch
a horseless carriage chug precariously down the road, while women
tittered and men swore and wild-eyed horses trembled in their har-
nesses. It was quite an event in those days, when a horseless carriage
took to the road.

And it is equally difficult for me, today, to watch the elaborate
indifference of a modern city when the great medical men of the
world come and go, and make their significant speeches to a limited
audience, rating little attention from the press . . . while at the same
time recalling the rather enthusiastic welcome that was extended to
me back in 1904 when I first decided to establish a practice in Los
Angeles.

I don't mean by this that I was handed the key to the city or had to
fight my way through showers of confetti while waving magnanimously to the assembled brass bands. But I soon became aware of a
certain awed respect from my contemporaries in the medical profession, entirely unwarranted by the facts. I was the fair-haired boy from
Boston. My studies in Europe had endowed me with a certain prestige;

and the richly deserved respect for men with whom I had been associated somehow reflected upon me.

I do not recall any particular modesty that caused me to protest the
respect being afforded me. I am afraid I took it pretty much for
granted, and it is only in later years after observing the casual acceptance ot truly great men in the medical field that the irony of the
situation has become whimsically apparent. But that, I'm afraid, is the
way of the world. A one-cylinder horseless carriage in 1904 received
more attention than does a sixteen-cylinder limousine in 1951. And
the same ratio possibly holds true in other fields, including that of
psychiatry.

I had been in Los Angeles but a couple of years, when I was invited
to meet with a number of colleagues and consider the urgent need for
establishing a medical school in Los Angeles. The founding of the
College of Physicians and Surgeons resulted from that meeting, and I
was honored by the appointment as assistant Dean, in addition to
serving as professor of psychiatry. Later, when the growing school
was urgently in need of an endowment in order to continue operation,
I was privileged to enter into the negotiations which resulted in its
acceptance as the medical school of the University of Southern California.

During these years, leading up to 1913, I was a member of the Los
Angeles Athletic Club. And somehow, without premeditation, a group
of us drifted into the habit of meeting in the Blue Room on Saturdays
to discuss world destiny, the high or low tariff, and the relative merits
of olives vs. lemon peel in a dry martini.

I sat one afternoon with Harry Haldeman, a leading industrialist,
and with Lloyd Moultrie, a prominent attorney. And somewhere
amidst the casual drift of the conversation we commenced discussing
the advantages of having a private little community with a clubroom
and a common square—summer homes and week-end cottages, or
full-time residences for those who might be interested. And as we
talked that afternoon our dreams became more roseate, and the back-
slapping became more boisterous. "I tell you, Harry ol' pal, there's

nothing in the world finer than to have good friends. Good fellow-ship! That's the stuff!"

From this and from other talks and dreams was born the Uplifters Club ... although my seven-year-old daughter after dubious observa-tion somehow got the impression that it was the Cuplifters Club, an observation worthy of the Out-of-the-Mouths-of-Babes Department.

Among the early members was a gum-chewing rope-twirler by the name of Will Rogers, destined to become the symbolized spirit of the club, and across the boulevard from the original property stands the Rogers Ranch, while the Will Rogers Polo Field nestles in the heart of the property itself.

Members of the Uplifters Club in those halcyon days were mostly men of wealth and prominence, from all the fields of arts and science, politics and commerce. And yet there existed a peculiar type of con-centrated democracy, for men were appraised by what they were and not by who they were. I have seen unknown entertainers treated as cordially as governors, and on other occasions I have seen governors quietly ushered out, not to return. There existed but a single yard-stick: Members or guests, drunk or sober, must conduct themselves as gentlemen at all times. And I doubt if a three-volume index of laws and by-laws could have served the purpose so well.

I've sometimes thought in later years that our noble experiment in building up a civilization could perhaps profit from an equally simple approach—if we could trade off a hundred thousand statutes in ex-change for the golden rule, and recognize a responsibility to guide the oncoming generations while forgetting this great ambition to mold them.

Just as life in general became more complicated when the unicellular organisms snuggled up together to form a higher type of animal, so did human life become more complicated when man commenced to organize into a higher type of society. Each individual became more dependent upon his neighbors, and more completely at their mercy.

And I suppose it is more-or-less natural that there should appear uniform laws, books of etiquette, religious precepts, widespread super-stitions, and Lifebuoy ads in magazines. Using the weapons of fear, ridicule, contempt, and threats of physical violence or social ostracism, man has attempted a colossal job of organization to hold the human herd together . . . and to make each random sample look and act and think and smell as much like any other random sample as is humanly possible.

The legendary hunk of human clay is neatly pressed into the pre-built mold. And through a psychological process of artificial insemination, a highly refined conscience is planted within the mind of the individual and nurtured through the years of childhood. And many of the lessons are driven home not wisely but too well.

The home, the church, and the school, all unite in a three-front attack to frighten Junior away from the pitfalls of transgression and to beckon him toward the ultimate virtues.

Society strives to protect itself from the misdeeds of the individual by spinning for him a tight web of inhibition and repression, woven into the mantle of his conscience. But like a tourniquet, it can be drawn too tight and left too long—to ultimately destroy that which it had set out to save.

The extent of that destruction commenced to give me insomnia in the years leading up to World War I when I was serving as Superintendent of the Los Angeles Psychopathic Hospital, and serving regularly as a member of the Lunacy Commission. Both of these were part-time jobs, in addition to my lectures at the university and the maintenance of a private practice, but they commenced to etch permanent wrinkles upon my forehead, and to produce worries about the future of the world long before I'd ever heard of an atom bomb.

The Lunacy Commission met regularly once or twice a week, and later three times a week as the volume of business continued to grow. The commission consisted of a superior court judge, another psychiatrist, and myself. And in actual practice, it became a rapid-fire, wholesale business—with as many as forty to sixty patients to be examined and committed or rejected.

Many of these persons, of course, came before the commission after confinement in the Psychopathic Hospital, and in those cases I had

the advantage of previous examination, and the procedure of commitment was little more than a legal technicality.

There were some rejections, naturally. Almost always there are
overzealous relatives a bit too eager to push grandma or grandpa off
the family's budget and onto the state's; willing to make a bid for a
mental institution when the County Poor Farm has hung out its "No-
Vacancy" sign. There are also attempts to railroad a perfectly lucid
and normal individual for reasons that are selfish or malicious; although it happens rather less often in fact than in fiction. But the
great bulk of the endless parade is composed of those who are urgently
in need of such help as the state can provide, or such confinement as
society can afford for its own protection. The routine work of a
lunacy commission is not something to be observed by an individual
with a sensitive soul and a sensitive stomach. It is a very disheartening
business.

At the Psychopathic Hospital, aside from intelligent attempts at
diagnosis and observation, I think it is reasonably accurate to say that
we administered one type of therapy and prescribed but a single
medicine: the methodical passage of time. Nor should this be sneered
at too contemptuously, for the passage of time remains the world's
great healer, outstripping the most celebrated of the miracle drugs. In
confinement, sheltered from the pricks and barbs of an unpleasant life
in the outside world, even some of the more advanced psychotics may
gradually return toward the mental and emotional norm and become
eligible for eventual discharge.

The Psychopathic Hospital served largely as a front-line first-aid
station in society's battle for survival. Here we took in the mental
and emotional casualties from the struggle, placed them under observation, and graduated the psychotics to the Lunacy Commission and
thence on to the state's mental institutions. Meanwhile, we could do
little more than to wage battle against constipation and auto-intoxica-
tion, and make use of the tepid bath.

Most everyone, I imagine, has noticed the soothing and calming
effects of a warm bath. It invites relaxation, dissolves the accumulated
jitters, and often will be followed by refreshing sleep. The body itself

is composed largely of water, and before the myriad cells could cuddle
up together and form a higher type of animal capable of striking out
away from the seashore, they had to reckon with the problem of making each living organism a sort of self-contained reservoir. The skin,
however, heavily fortified with nerve endings, is exposed to the sur-
rounding atmosphere, and the air in our homes is often more lacking
in moisture than is the air over the Sahara Desert. Thus, in theory at
least, the tepid bath is something like Old Home Week for the cells,
forming the outer guard of the human body. They relax, in the kind
of environment where all life began. The jangled nerves which had
been deluged with all kinds of grumbling complaints from the sentries,
of the skin, find the traffic considerably reduced. And if the outer
cells of the body were capable of purring like kittens, they would no
doubt do so. To that extent, the esprit de corps is improved, with
better morale in the front-line trenches.

But with or without the theories, we had to depend largely upon
the tepid bath because little else was available. We had no shock
treatments then. No pentothal sodium. None of the modern miracles
which have come through years of increased discovery. When the
patient became too tense, excited, and uncontrollable, he went into the
big drink, and there he might be kept for many hours. More formally,
we referred to it as hydrotherapy.

But it wasn't always a beautiful sight, like the colored pictures of
bathing beauties relaxing in the crystal-clear waters of some land-
scaped spa. Patients were sometimes violent. The excrement from
their bodies often gave the room a nauseating odor, and the two
indispensable requirements of an attendant were a strong body and a
strong stomach.

It was not the most pleasant type of work in the world. And because
of limited budgets, it didn't pay the best money in the world. The
duties of an attendant or an orderly combined the techniques of a
wrestler, a lifeguard, a street cleaner, a chambermaid, and a youngster
at a Halloween party bobbing for apples.

There weren't enough physicians, psychiatrists, or trained nurses
even to make an impression upon the daily volume of work. And I

was appalled, at first, to observe the kind of persons who composed a large share of the staff and upon whom, in the final analysis, it was necessary to depend for the actual treatment of patients. But through the years my respect for these overworked and underpaid nonprofessional employees rose to the level of admiration. Two fervent hopes I have held: I hope no one near and dear to me ever has to spend any time in a psychopathic hospital; and if this is too much to ask, then I hope they don't have to spend their time in such an institution as nonprofessional hired help. I know of no other group of people who have to give so much and who have to take so much; and yet who receive so very little.

It would be foolish, of course, to imply that this endless and increasing parade of the mentally abnormal and the emotionally unstable is due entirely to our efforts to push each new hunk of human clay into a pre-selected mold. You'll find no single villain in the plot. And yet there's evidence that a fair share of the responsibility must be shouldered by our overzealousness in drawing tight the two corset-strings of a tight-fitting conscience—inhibition and repression.

Ray M. and Frank J. offer an interesting contrast in the matter of conscience. Using the yardstick of normality, Ray M. suffered from too little, and Frank J. from too much.

Without going into their histories too completely, Ray was an accused criminal who'd pleaded not guilty by reason of insanity. Frank was a suspected psychotic, brought before the Lunacy Commission for confinement to a mental institution.

Despite his subtle efforts to appear abnormal, neither I nor two other psychiatrists could offer conclusive evidence of mental illness in Ray M. He was accused of having embezzled a large amount of money over a period of years, of striking and killing his employer, and of attempting to burn down the garage where he had been employed, in an effort to destroy the evidence.

Apparently he had struck his employer with a heavy tool of some kind, fracturing the skull, and then soaked the body with gasoline before applying a match. And then with a burst of efficiency, he had piled up ledgers, vouchers, receipts, and so on, forming a funeral pyre of all the disputed records.

He was a very frightened and apprehensive young man at the time of the examination, but there was no evidence that he was troubled to any great extent with a guilty conscience. Reminded that his employer left a wife and child, he responded in almost pleading tones: "What about me? I've got a wife and kid, too. And they won't have insurance money to go on if they pin this thing on me."

With the negative findings of the psychiatric examination, Ray M. was found guilty. But because there was no evidence of premeditation, the death penalty was not asked and he was sentenced to life imprisonment.

Frank J., inversely, displayed an overactive conscience. Because he had accidentally stepped on a beetle several weeks earlier, he had since refused to leave his room except when brought, forcefully, before the commission. Asked about it, his face twisted with agony and he almost sobbed. "It had as much right to live as I have. Probably more right, because it didn't kill, and I did. I killed it. 'Thou shalt not kill,' our Father says. But I killed it. Forgive me, Father, I know not what I do."

There was, of course, a long history of strange behavior—weeks of withdrawal and deep melancholy, a conviction of personal worthlessness, and the episode of the beetle is merely illustrative. But it helps to place Frank J. in the opposite corner from Ray M. in the matter of conscience and how tightly it is wound.

Because of facts brought to light in the case, it was considered wise to commit Frank to a mental institution. But here the contrast of the two cases becomes even more impressive:

Here are two men. Roughly stated, one could not be given his freedom because he lacked the self-discipline and restraint that conscience is supposed to provide. The other had to be confined because a tightly drawn conscience restricted him from normal social behavior. One is a criminal and the other is a psychotic.

But significantly, the state is generally better prepared to provide adequate facilities for the criminal than for the psychotic; more willing to spend adequate funds for his daily care. The jury in a criminal case is not called upon to temper its verdict with the consideration of whether or not space is available for the man's confinement. But this consideration must weigh eternally upon the members of the Lunacy Commission.

Significantly, too, the relatives of the psychotic will be equally evasive when faced with a direct question: "Where's your cousin Frank these days? I haven't seen him around."

It would be foolish to imply that environment, alone, could be held accountable for making these two men what they were. In the case of Frank J., particularly, the family history was shot through with records of mental illness, giving a broad hint of hereditary tainting. But these are the extremes. And in between will be found the great masses of more nearly normal individuals. These are the ones who constitute all but the fringe of our society. And there can be little doubt that early environment plays a decisive role in determining how snugly the conscience is going to fit.

The human offspring arrives in the world with but a few stream-lined instincts, a total lack of prejudice, and a pair of simple fears . . . but with an infinite capacity for acquiring more as he goes along.

He has no inborn fear of mice, men, or matrimony. He has no pre-destined flavor preference for cherry pie or whale blubber. He has no instinctive knowledge of property rights and hence no inborn aversion to stealing. He has no inherent love of truth and his ability to separate truth from falsehood must be learned—usually the hard way—during his first few years of life.

He starts out as a Lilliputian in a land of giants, dependent upon adults for his care and for his survival. But he is not immediately aware of his individuality. In the family group he is merely a member of the team. The love and care and attentions he receives are pretty much taken for granted. To him, it is no more remarkable that his mother should tend his needs, than it is that his own hands should reach out and grasp his rattle. The umbilical cord was snipped at the time of birth, physically separating his body from that of his mother.

But the psychic cord remains untouched and should ordinarily dissolve through the passing years.

The child who gets his fair share of love and who feels perfectly secure within his family group has no particular need for feelings of uneasiness, even though he slowly becomes aware of his own physical and mental inferiority in a world run by adults. He knows, somehow, that those who love him will guard him and tend his needs.

The child who is denied his fair quota of love may experience no such feelings of security. He is weaned, psychologically, at too early an age. He is not sure of his place in the family group, and he is more aware of himself as an individual—a very small individual whose very survival may be dependent upon the moods and whims and caprice of those unpredictable adults who flit across the horizon of his world.

His own physical and mental inferiority may frighten him. He may become acutely aware of that inferiority, and his subconscious mind may soberly file away attitudes and impressions that can never be completely erased. He may nourish the seeds of fears that can never be totally conquered. And interspersed with these, in a random mix, may be the seeds of bitter hatred.

Because they want a child they can be proud of, and one who'll impress the neighbors and fit the standard pattern of How-the-Well-Disciplined-Child-Will-Behave, parents launch all too soon into the program of "Ah! Ah! No no! Naughty! Naughty!" They draw the inhibitions ever tighter.

The child may become a mass of frustrations because Mama and Papa are striving too hard for social approval. They make his young life miserable with too many criticisms and too much coaching, and too frequent reversals of the field. He's not sure what's expected of him, but he knows it'll be wrong as soon as he does it.

This is the beginning of things. This is the child's environmental heritage. And through it all, the subconscious mind strives to find a way out of the situation at hand and to avoid a repetition of experiences that are unpleasant. Each time the emotions commence to boil, body chemistry goes upon a wartime footing. Digestion is interrupted. Blood pressure increases. The heart beats more rapidly. The chemical composition of the blood is altered. And the ultimate effect of all this is both mental and physical—to such an extent that the imaginary dividing line between the two becomes no longer discernible.

An experienced building inspector, I understand, can look at the foundation of a structure and pretty well tell whether the contractor has chiseled a bit too much on materials; used an improper ratio of cement to sand and gravel, or performed an inadequate job of mixing and tamping. And it is perhaps no more phenomenal that a trained psychiatrist can look at a potential draftee and do a fair job of judging whether he experienced an emotionally normal life during the years when his body was being built and when the expression lines of his face were being broken in.

The fears and rebellions and apprehensions and hatreds of childhood are not merely psychological experiences. They help to determine the ratio and distribution of materials from which the body is built. And from this, the actual physical structure of the body is directly affected.

Potential points of weakness in the body may develop in those organs that were short-changed during the emotionally disturbed periods of childhood. The subconscious mind operates its own rationing board during periods of emotional stress, and the various organs of the body must develop as best they can on restricted quotas during the crucial growing period. Nor can these shortages be conveniently compensated for later on. It is a little difficult to come back later and add more cement to the mixture in a foundation after the concrete is set, and after the inspector has discovered the weakness.

The psychosomatic theory finds a close relationship between personality types and certain pathological ailments. But there is in it nothing truly ingenious, and it marks no peculiar triumph for the medical profession. The qualified engineer can quite accurately predict where the faults will appear in a building that lacks the proper foundation support. The qualified mechanic can predict where trouble will develop in the wartime-produced machine that was built with substitute alloy gears because nothing better was available at the time. And why shouldn't the qualified psychiatrist and physician be able to

# A FEW BUTTONS MISSING

predict where future trouble may develop in a human body that was built while the emotions were too often upon an emergency basis?

There seems little doubt from this point on that personality types are largely determined by childhood experiences. And with the family being what it is, a very large share of the responsibility points back directly to parental influence.

Laurene S. came to my office voluntarily because she had an uncontrollable fear of confinement—claustrophobia. She couldn't force herself to ride in elevators or to enter other small enclosures. Even in a telephone booth, she admitted, she made a practice of leaving the door open. As far back as she could remember, she had adjusted herself quite well to the phobia and it had not particularly affected her way of life. But she had recently married and her husband was growing a little weary of climbing stairs to keep her company, in buildings equipped with perfectly reliable elevators.

"He thinks I'm very silly," Laurene told me, "and I realize that I am. He keeps telling me that nobody lives forever, and that if a cable should break we'd both go down together. He thinks it's very odd that I should be afraid to ride in an elevator, but I'm not afraid to have him ride in one. And he keeps telling me that anybody can do anything, if they just put their mind to it. But I just can't do it."

She explained that she wasn't afraid of a cable breaking. She wasn't afraid of being killed. "Really, I don't feel that I'm afraid of anything in particular," she insisted. "It's just something that I can't force myself to do."

When I helped her to go probing back through a lot of old and neglected memories that had been stored for years in her subconscious mind, she recalled that her parents had locked her in the closet as a form of punishment when she was very small.

One incident in particular she recalled. Her father had demanded that she "confess" writing on the outside walls of the house with a colored crayon. Circumstantial evidence all pointed to little Laurene, but actually, she told me, she hadn't done it. And she'd refused to say she had.

Her father, in a fit of temper, had locked her in the closet while he shouted outside the door: "By God, I'll leave you in there until you rot, if you can't learn to tell the truth! I'd rather not have a daughter, than to have one who's a liar."

It was dark in the closet, Laurene explained, and the inside of the door had no handle on it. She'd pounded furiously against the door with her tiny fists, screaming over and over, "I didn't do it! I didn't! I didn't!" But finally, in a state of hysterical exhaustion she'd conceded the point. "All right, I did do it, but let me out of here." The father, however, had decided to give her a little more time to reflect upon the error of her ways. "I'll think it over," he'd announced grimly, "and I'll let you know later what I've decided." And little Laurene had spent another hour in the closet, sobbing and shivering, and, in childish gullibility, wondering how long it would take a person inside a closet to commence to rot.

From that dramatic but ill-advised attempt to teach her a lesson in truthfulness and to cinch up her conscience another notch, Mr. S. had helped to consign his daughter to a life of emotional abnormality and to embarrassment destined to extend through many years.

It is significant that Laurene's reaction in this incident had not been one of simple, unadulterated fear—such as one might experience upon meeting a tiger on a jungle trail. Involved also were feelings of disillusionment, a loss of faith in absolute justice, hatred of the father, and a sense of shame because of that hatred.

Such highly involved and often conflicting emotions are almost inevitable in the child-parent relationship, illustrating the truth of the adage that we most deeply hurt those whom we love the most.

An entirely different type of case was that of Albert J., who came to my office to consult me as a physician and not as a psychiatrist. He was a near neighbor and a close friend, and he complained of a recent attack of acute indigestion. "I can't seem to get completely over it," he told me. "I'm probably silly to make such a fuss about it, but it took all the starch out of me and I can't get it back."

"Have you had these attacks before?" I asked.

He shrugged. "I used to have a touchy stomach about the time I was in college. Not so much in recent years." But he went on to explain that he'd eaten some tainted seafood at a small restaurant. "It didn't taste too fresh, but I didn't think too much of it at the time," he told me. "Then the next morning it hit me. Fran had to practically carry me upstairs to bed."

The description was a little incongruous, for he was a heavy man, weighing nearly two hundred pounds, while his wife, I knew, was a fragile little thing of the China doll type.

"You're sure it was indigestion?" I asked, and he nodded his head.

"It was that seafood, I tell you. The minute the thing hit me, I knew exactly what it was. Sharp pains, something like the heartburn I used to have. An awful lot of gas on my stomach. I suppose, actually, it was a form of poisoning. What worries me is the fact that I don't seem to snap out of it completely."

So far as I know, nothing else was said that could have hinted at anything wrong, aside from an attack of indigestion or food poisoning, and his seafood story was quite impressive. And yet I insisted that he visit a colleague of mine for an electrocardiograph examination of his heart. Why? Well, simply because he was the type of person who should be on guard for the first signs of coronary thrombosis and because, in certain circumstances, the pains can resemble those of acute indigestion. He was a large man, a little too pudgy. And obesity in itself is a hint of potential circulatory disorders, just as a four-ton load on a two-ton truck is a hint of potential mechanical troubles.

But more than that, he was a successful man. I knew that he had struggled to put himself through college. After that he had started in a minor position in a large corporation, and had in remarkably short time worked his way up to the presidency. With no money to start with, and with nothing more than his labors and his ingenuity, he had acquired a substantial share of the company's stock. He had married late in life, choosing a mate years younger than himself, and one of the leading socialites of the city. In short, the story of his life had been the kind of story that Horatio Alger might have gloated over. But it contained one hint that Horatio Alger never thought to mention: It qualified my friend as reasonably typical of a potential coronary case.

However, the electrocardiograph reports quickly eliminated the word "potential." Albert J.'s attack of "acute indigestion" had been a coronary thrombosis, and I left him under the care of my colleague who was a specialist in that field.

In modesty, I should admit that it was merely a lucky guess on my part that I sent my friend to a heart specialist, instead of advising him to be more careful about eating tainted seafood. But it is remarkable how consistently lucky one's guesses may become, after he has observed the achievements in the field of psychosomatic medicine.

I was never able to compile a complete case history of my friend, Albert J. What little I know of his background is mostly knowledge acquired in purely social conversation, prior to the time of his call to my office. Unfortunately, he died a few months after the visit.

But I do know that he had been a stubborn, headstrong youngster with an overwhelming urge to excel. On several occasions I heard him laughingly tell of the time when he and a group of older boys at a public plunge had competed to stay under water for the greatest length of time, and he had eventually been fished out by the lifeguard and given artificial respiration. "Silliest damn thing I ever did," he used to chuckle, then slap his knee and add proudly, "but by George, I won by a mile!"

What kindled in Albert's young heart this great urge to surpass others? Here we can merely speculate—but the speculation may be guided by the findings in hundreds of similar cases where the investigation was more complete. And once again the finger points accusingly toward early parental influence.

The competitive urge comes early to this personality type. Often it is born of the son's competition with the father, in seeking the affections of the mother and wife. The child, instead of being supremely confident of maternal love and affection, finds himself being rationed. Often he is the subject of home-brewed psychology, where hugs and kisses and other tangible forms of affection are reserved as special awards of merit. "That's a very good boy to tell Mama when you have to go toy-toy. Here's a great big kiss!" And the child at an early age gets the impression that he is loved, not for what he is, but for what he achieves.

It's a tiny seed when planted, but it may grow through the years until the urge to excel and to achieve and to surpass others becomes the very core of life itself.

My friend Albert J., for example, was soberly warned after his first coronary that he must take life easy, avoid undue exertion and emotional strain. Actually, it shouldn't have been difficult. He had more money than he could conceivably need for the rest of his life, and no children to leave it to. The corporation he headed could have continued without so much as a slight stagger after his resignation, just as it did after his death. Hundreds of eager persons were waiting to take over his social and civic duties.

"I've been silly a lot of times in my life, but I'm not exactly a fool," he told me, when the exact nature of his illness became known. "I'm going to spend the rest of my time just taking life easy. I'm going to catch up on a lot of sleep I've lost through the years."

For several weeks, his wife told me later, he did take it easy. But then the smouldering fires of unrest became too much for him. The ravenous hunger for achievement was more than he could withstand. And he was at his desk in the midst of a reorganization program when the final attack came.

The cause of death? Coronary thrombosis. That's what it said on the death certificate. A clot had shut off the flow of blood to muscles of the heart. This is real, and physical, and mechanical. But there is reason to believe that the real cause of death could be traced far back through the years.

Like so many psychosomatic ailments, it was a case of unpremeditated murder, equipped with a delayed action fuse.

In our most humble and sincere efforts to restrict and confine our children and to tighten the tourniquet of social inhibitions, we undoubtedly trace the pattern of many future tragedies. It is the unfortunate result of attempting to enforce too many rules—of struggling too hard to make children "good," and striving too little to make them happy and contented.

It may be beautifully poetic to speak of children as "bits of human clay who need to be molded." But it is very poor psychology. Children are little bits of living protoplasm, who need merely to be guided.

# 10

*He who reigns within himself and rules his passions,*
*desires and fears is more than a king.*—MILTON

To MY GRANDFATHER and perhaps to yours, any pain in the region
of the abdomen was known simply and eloquently as a bellyache.
Grandpa didn't know the difference between indigestion and chronic
or acute appendicitis, and he gazed with suspicion upon any person
using polysyllabic words. "Don't make no difference what you call it
anyhow. It's still a bellyache." With that conviction he lived, and with
that conviction he died. (Possibly from a ruptured appendix.)

It took many years of education to drive home the lesson that not
all pains of the abdomen are identical; that they frequently present
different symptoms and spring from different causes. Millions of gov-
ernment pamphlets have been sent out postage-free to the young
mothers of the nation. Adult education classes have stressed What to
Do Until the Doctor Comes. American advertising has portrayed the
hazards of a vitamin deficiency, the social implications of pink tooth-
brush, and the more easily recognized symptoms of athlete's foot.

But mental disorders, unfortunately, have never been so fully explained, nor can they be discussed so casually.

Technically speaking, the term insanity is a legal and not a medical
term. It's a question for the courts to decide. Uncle Herman may
swear up and down that he's a canary and perch all day on the rim of
the bathtub. But he is not really "insane" until he has been formally
committed. In our democracy, every man is innocent until he is
proved guilty; and every man is sane until he is proved insane.

With that handy and all-inclusive term removed, there are remarkably few terms left for ordinary conversation. It is possible to say, "I'm afraid Uncle Herman is mentally ill." But it sounds a little too formal and a little too pedantic. To refer to his behavior as "queer" brings a connotation not justified by the facts of the case. So those things may be by-passed by the layman, in favor of the somber concession that poor old Uncle Herman doesn't have all his buttons, or the blunt conjecture that the old boy is nuttier than a fruit cake.

The formal language of psychiatry is not suitable for public use, any more than the botanical names of flowers are suitable for the home gardener. With other worries on his mind, who wants to learn to pronounce and to correctly spell such terms as schizophrenia, paranoia, melancholia, and so on?

Surely there will be an honored place in the Hall of Fame for the man who will patiently introduce simple, effective, and distinctive work-a-day names for the various mental disorders, so that they may be used with confidence by the layman without the eternal fear of a misplaced accent bringing gasps of horror from a maiden aunt.

At one time during the days of my professorship, I secured two large photographs of wrecked automobiles and took them to class. Both cars had been nearly demolished, and the photographs had been used in a display to promote the sale of automotive insurance.

"What I want to do," I told the class, "is to test your ingenuity. I want you to study these pictures, observe the nature and the extent of the damage, and tell me how the accidents happened."

The assignment, difficult though it was, was greeted with a certain amount of enthusiasm. The students studied the pictures with painstaking care. I could overhear them discussing such things as "direction of force" and "points of impact." "You can tell by the way this radiator is smashed in, that it hit something head-on. Then it must have rolled over, to cave in the top like that."

But in the end, when the written appraisals were submitted, there was no uniformity whatsoever in the estimates of what had caused the accidents to cars *A* and *B*. Some thought car *A* had hit a telephone pole while traveling at a high rate of speed, while car *B* had been hit by a train. Others had it figured out exactly the opposite.

Actually, I told them later, car *A* had gone over a cliff, flipped end over end many times; but contrary to all logic, reason, or common sense, the lower half of the windshield had remained unbroken. Car *B* had been innocently parked at the curb at the time of an explosion within a nearby building. Both had been examples of freak accidents, against which a cautious motorist should be insured.

"The point is," I told the class, "that we must never confuse the visible symptoms with the cause of the trouble itself. We must not arbitrarily assume that all automobiles with smashed radiators have run into telephone poles. And we must not assume that all patients with similar hallucinations suffer similar disorders, springing from similar causes."

The point, I think, is basic. And altogether too often, even the more learned of medical men become so absorbed in classifying symptoms that they lose sight of the ailments themselves.

What specific value could there be in it, if a highway safety engineer compiled monthly reports of mechanical "symptoms"? "Last month there were seventeen smashed radiators, forty-nine crumpled fenders, eleven broken windshields, and two cars completely demolished." Such statistics might be of some interest to a man who's considering the purchase of an automotive body-and-fender repair shop, but they would be of little value in planning an intelligent program to increase highway safety.

To make the study of value, the engineer would have to go beyond the mere mechanical symptoms to consider the nature and the cause of the various accidents: seven failures to yield the right of way; nine failures to stop at arterial intersections, and one head-on collision as the result of passing on a blind corner. But even these statistics don't reach down to the very roots of the problems. The efficient analyst of such statistics will want to know, also, the causes of these respective failures. Has there been insufficient highway safety education? Are dangerous intersections sufficiently posted with warning signs? Is there adequate speed control on the sections of highway where the most accidents occur? Are there hazardous curves that could be eliminated? When these things are investigated, the safety engineer is approaching the problem itself and not merely the symptomatic outposts.

In exactly the same way, the classification of mental disorders must go far beyond the mere classification of apparent symptoms. To have significance, the maladies must be sorted out according to causes, and not according to results. And this fact offers little promise for the home analysis.

It is significant, I think, that the body-and-fender repairmen outnumber the safety engineers by a ratio of many hundred to one. And I'm afraid the same ratio holds true in psychiatry and in many other fields. An ounce of prevention may be worth a pound of cure, but it is more than sixteen times as scarce.

Generally speaking, the persons who need the services of a psychiatrist may be divided into two broad divisions—the psychotics and the neurotics. Neither fits the pattern of the mentally normal. Each may suffer delusions, although it might be more truthful to say that the neurotics suffer delusions while the psychotics often seem to enjoy them.

The advanced psychotic has drifted off to his dream world and tied his ship fast to the far shore. The neurotic may find himself drifting toward such a state of unreality but he struggles frantically against the tide, and attempts to fight his way back toward the world of normality he has previously known.

Nor will the neurosis develop into a psychosis if left unattended, any more than a neglected case of hives will progress into smallpox.

By and large, the psychotics are the ones who populate the mental institutions while the neurotics may be found in endless numbers in physicians' waiting rooms. But this is a very broad generality.

From a medical standpoint, the psychosis may represent the more difficult problem and might conceivably be described as the more serious malady. But from a social standpoint there's ample reason to believe that the neurotic constitutes the greater problem of the two.

In 1909, because of a legal question concerning a relative's estate, I was called upon to examine a psychotic patient named Fred C., who had been confined to a southern California medical hospital for twelve years. I learned that he hadn't spoken a dozen words in all that time. Only rarely would he nod or shake his head in reply to questions. He would take no part in any activities, but stood most of the time staring into space. On rare occasions, without warning or provocation, he would attack another patient. But the attacks were neither serious nor prolonged, and he would promptly sink again into his apathy, staring into space. Except for the space he occupied and the cost of his minimum needs and care, he was no particular problem either to the staff or to the world at large. Merely a living corpse.

In private practice, at the same time, I was concerned with a Mrs. Wanda I., who was a neurotic, and the mother of five young children, including two sets of twins. She was a woman of average intelligence and the wife of a reasonably prosperous businessman. To her friends, neighbors, and casual acquaintances, I'm quite sure she appeared as a fairly normal woman, a little touchy about matters of diet and of rather fragile health—but quite normal, for all that. "Good heavens! There's no reason why she should be seeing a psychiatrist!"

And yet, within her own home, she was alternately a whining invalid and a screaming tyrant, inflicting extreme punishment upon her children for the violation of any of her infinite rules. When her husband would remonstrate with her because of her treatment of the children, she would scream at him that she was a sick woman. And usually after such a scene she would take to her bed and remain there for several days. How her husband had ever induced her to seek psychiatric help I don't know. But she was resentful and uncoöperative from the outset, and could not be depended upon to keep her appointments. She was entirely indifferent when I informed her that I would have to charge her for appointments broken without any advance notice. "Just send the bill. That's all you have to do." And I discovered that the financial responsibility for the family was shouldered entirely by the husband, while she made no attempt to conserve in any way.

"A man can stand just so much," her husband told me miserably, when I called him to my office for a private interview. "I used to try to reason with her, when she'd go on a spree and start spending money too recklessly. But it never did any good. She'd get upset, and I'd get upset. And when I got too upset I couldn't take care of my business. I just let her have her head, and hope to God that I can earn money faster than she can spend it. Ordinarily she isn't too bad about it."

The same attitude, I discovered, concerned the care of the children. "What good does it do to bat your head against a brick wall?" he asked me. "I discovered that when I said anything about it, things always got worse instead of better. So I just hold my tongue and go about my business, and pretend not to notice. And I keep hoping that everything will work out all right in the long run."

But it was, I'm afraid, a rather futile hope. For here was a woman wielding a terrific influence over five small children during the most important years of their lives—planting the seeds of future neuroses and sketching the plot of potential tragedies. Not only was her own life made miserable, but it was affecting the lives of those around her.

As I got further into the case, I discovered that the husband had been seeking solace from the proverbial "other woman." But such unfaithfulness weighed heavily upon his conscience, and was gradually driving him away from normality. I never met the "other woman" in the case—but it is a reasonably safe assumption that the situation caused her a certain amount of mental anguish and disillusionment also.

The psychiatrist who fails to win the confidence and receive the coöperation of his neurotic patient must concede failure at the first and most crucial hurdle. And without excuse or apology, I will confess that I have failed many patients through the years. I am afraid that almost any psychiatrist would have to make a similar confession. For even with the most subtle psychology, it becomes largely a matter of leading the horse to water.

I was never able to overcome Mrs. Wanda I.'s open hostility. Neither was I able to convince her that she should seek the services of another psychiatrist in whom she might have more confidence. Her marriage ended in divorce court several years later, with the seeds of many tragedies sown along the way.

Neither was I nor anyone else able to help Fred C. He lived out his days inside mental institutions.

That is why it is difficult to state arbitrarily that the psychoses are more serious maladies than are the neuroses. A lot depends upon where you're sitting, and how broad a view you take.

With his emotional blunting or strange hallucinations or highly peculiar behavior pattern, the psychotic lives in a world of his own, and in reasonably complete isolation. He may be confined, physically, to an institution. But he is first confined mentally. He may be treated with a certain amount of resigned tolerance by others within the home, but his comments and suggestions are subject to a hundred percent discount. He may cause embarrassment and concern to the family, and in some cases he may be responsible for physical violence. But aside from these things, he shoulders his own burden in his own isolated world.

The typical neurotic, on the other hand, may rebel at isolation and might be compared in effect to the man with impetigo who nevertheless insists upon attending the Annual Sun Bathers' Picnic. In a manner of speaking, neuroses are contagious. And the neurotic mother often teaches all the fine points of irrational behavior to her offspring, thus causing the malady to become a fine old family tradition that spreads down through successive generations.

From an economic standpoint, neuroses are expensive. They may funnel off a large share of the family income for pink pills and placebos, medical care and surgical operations, alimony payments and frantic trips in the futile search for health.

More people in the United States each year are bitten by dogs than are bitten by tigers. Tigers, generally, are kept isolated in cages while dogs are maintained as family pets. And roughly the same general comparison might apply to the advanced psychotics who are confined to mental institutions, and to the mildly neurotic individuals who have the run of the neighborhood.

The psychotic, generally speaking, seeks his isolation as an avenue of escape. He retreats to his dream world when, for one reason or another, he finds it impossible to continue on in the rather dreary workaday world where the rest of us struggle and worry and live. He is a difficult patient to treat for he has no desire to be cured.

Today he is Napoleon. He has wealth, and power, and fame, and prestige. He is ruler of all he surveys. Give him a smile and a pat on the back and he may magnanimously grant you a throne or bequeathe you half an empire, and then sit back and reflect upon the benevolence of his own generosity.

He is not impressed by the offer of the courier who promises to take him back to another world where he will be Joe Jones, third assistant pick-up man on the city garbage truck and the marital mate of a sharp-tongued wench who's eternally prattling about the other men she could have married. No thank you. He prefers to keep on being Napoleon. And he finds Josephine much more interesting.

Or possibly the psychotic is not Napoleon. He grants no favors and he dreams no dreams. Like Fred C., he sits vacant-eyed and uncomprehending, staring into space, isolated from the world by a vacuum; immersed in a social anaesthetic that protects him from all the barbs and pin-pricks of an unhappy mortal life. His body lives but his soul has died. He has committed psychic suicide, and he has no urgings to return to a world once found unbearable.

The claim has been made—and not without logic—that psychotics are just like everybody else, only a little more so. Certainly all the factors that go into the making of a psychosis or a neurosis will be found to some degree in those who are entirely normal. And mental abnormality is largely a percentage business.

In time of great emotional shock, such as the sudden and unexpected loss of a loved one, even a normal person may lapse into a complete stupor. Several years ago I chanced to arrive at the scene of an automobile accident shortly after it happened. A small Mexican girl had been struck and instantly killed by a heavy truck. The child's mother, a large woman, sat on the curb moaning softly and rocking slowly to right and left. Her eyes were completely blank, and she gave no sign of recognition when spoken to. The world of reality had suddenly become too grim for her to face and she had retreated into a state of stupor closely resembling that of the advanced schizophrenic. One might almost say that the greatest difference between the two states is hardly more than a matter of time. This mother, a normal woman, returned to face reality in a matter of minutes, while the psychotic remains away longer, or returns not at all.

Illusions, delusions, and hallucinations—generally conspicuous in psychoses—are also woven into the warp and the woof of everyday life. Manufacturers find that a can of soup will look larger and appear to be a better bargain and will sell more readily to the average housewife, if the label is designed and colored in a special pattern. It is illusion, pure and simple. The architect closes his eyes and visualizes the completed building roughly sketched on his drafting board; and he is observing a push-button hallucination. Disregarding all evidence and logic, a mother retains her unshakable faith in a worthless son and beholds his shortcomings as peculiar virtues; thereby preserving a delusion.

The process of identification with others is almost universal and almost eternal. Spectators at a ball game may lean in unison as they watch a fielder attempt to reach across a bleachers' barrier to catch a foul ball. The rabid fight fan in the balcony may spend a good share of the evening delivering left hooks and right crosses into thin air, as he identifies himself with one of the boxers within the ring. But most ludicrous of all, in my opinion, is to watch the spectators on the field during a track meet as they center their attention upon the high jumpers. At the very instant when the athlete commences his jump, the majority of the interested spectators will each lift one leg into the air like a ballet satire of a dog show. The spectators, of course, are not conscious of this or they surely wouldn't do it. But each has unconsciously associated himself with the athlete attempting to hurl himself across the bar. Physically, they are spectators. But emotionally, psychologically, and vicariously, each has become a competitor.

Surely there would be little suspense and little interest if we were unable to identify ourselves with the hero of a novel or of a radio or television or movie plot. Radio dramas, in particular, would be dismally drab affairs if the listeners merely heard the words and were unable to visualize poor Uncle Herman with his beard caught in a bear-trap.

Up to a certain point all of this is entirely normal. But the significant thing is this: The normal person leaves his illusions, delusions, and hallucinations behind when he puts down the book or walks out of the theatre, or snaps off the radio or television set. The psychotic just doesn't know when to quit. He has entered the land of vicarious association without bothering to buy a round-trip ticket.

# 11

*It is the little rift within the lute that by and by will make
the music mute, and ever widening slowly silence all.*
—TENNYSON

ON A NUMBER of occasions I have heard prominent and widely respected psychiatrists somberly proclaim that everyone in the world is
neurotic to a certain extent. From an illustrative standpoint it is undoubtedly a revealing observation. But it is, of course, a mathematical
absurdity—comparable to insisting that everyone in the world is slightly
below average.

The term neurosis is a man-invented classification, and with the
invention went the responsibility of establishing the approximate
boundaries. Obviously, if such a classification is to have significance
it must to some extent be exclusive. It can't include everybody. And
even though a reasonably normal individual may in modest degree
experience all of the emotions and reactions, and practice all of the
little self-deceptions typical of the neurotic, he is merely a pretender
to the title until he has mastered these things to an abnormal degree.

One of the sad things about being a psychiatrist is the fact that you
become acutely conscious of your own neurotic tendencies.

At one time during the tense days of World War I, I became
uncomfortably conscious of the fact that I was smoking too much.
Mechanically, through long habit, I'd light up a cigarette and puff
away at it while my conscious thoughts were far away. And then
would come bodily rebellion. A sudden nausea would strike me and

I'd hurriedly grind out the remains of the cigarette and inhale a little fresh, undiluted air.

This situation could be easily explained through simple mechanics: My body had become so saturated with nicotine poisoning through excessive smoking that it used this system to reduce the self-torture; to warn me to ease off a bit. But unfortunately at about this point I chanced to discover that the feeling of nausea would continue until I'd actually ground out the cigarette. If, as occasionally happened, I found myself in a place where it was necessary to walk outside to discard the burning cigarette, then the feeling of nausea would follow me all the way, and relief would commence only after I had physically gotten rid of the cigarette. The fact that I had quit puffing on it didn't seem to matter. Inversely, if I had an ash tray handy, I would immediately grind out the fire, and just as quickly the feeling of semi-nausea would stop.

These things would possibly pass unnoticed in the life of an average person. But to me they offered proof of a slight neurotic tendency. The rebellion came not from a nicotine-saturated body, but from a guilty conscience.

At one time during my professorship, a fellow member of the faculty confided to me that he'd cultivated a habit he was unable to break. A highly advertised soft drink had recently appeared on the market and he had become a toper.

"The damn stuff is habit forming," he told me seriously. "If I can't sneak out right after my ten o'clock class and get a bottle of it, I'm no good for the rest of the day."

This information came as somewhat of a shock to me, and although I'd heard very little about the drink, I determined to investigate. And a few days later I again confronted my friend.

"Where did you get this idea about your soft drink being habit forming?" I asked him, and he seemed a little amazed.

"Why, it's common knowledge. I thought everybody knew that. I think I even read something about it in the paper."

"That's just so much poppycock," I told him. "As far as I can find out, the stuff is no more habit forming than colored lemonade."

He insisted on arguing the point. But when I inquired again several weeks later he conceded that he'd been able to break the habit.

It is, I'd imagine, worth a great many millions of dollars to the tobacco industry, to preserve the legend that the habit of smoking is almost impossible to break. When the average man decides to swear off, or when he runs out of tobacco, he commences searching inwardly for that great and powerful yearning which he is sure will come. And no sooner does he search for it than he finds it. He refuses to believe that the smoking habit is merely a compilation of small mechanical habits, like cracking the knuckles or drumming the fingers on the edge of a desk. He is convinced that it embodies some chemical craving that has been built up in the body. And he forces himself to the humble concession that he's just naturally not the rugged type, who could suddenly swear off.

Tens of millions of persons smoke. And tens of millions will tell you that they're not men enough, or women enough, to quit. And so, by a process of mathematics, we must accept it as reasonably normal.

If there were only a few thousand smokers unable to quit, then we would call it a compulsive neurosis. By its very nature, a neurosis must be a minority report on the subject of human behavior.

Behind the smoking habit in most of us stands conflict: I-want-to-quit versus I-don't-want-to-quit; a fear of bodily harm from absorbing too much nicotine, versus a fear of an unsatisfied appetite from swearing off ... a virtual tag-team match of conflicting emotions and desires.

Similar conflicts may lead to other obsessive or compulsive acts which the individual is unable to stop at will. And when the behavior is such that it does not gain social acceptance as does the use of tobacco, then sooner or later the individual may find himself seeking psychiatric help.

The obsessive neurosis (psychasthenia) I have often compared to a phonograph record which has become scratched in such a way as to send the needle time and again into the same groove, repeating the same phrase over and over instead of getting on with the melody.

In effect, the subconscious mind keeps pestering the conscious mind with the same idea so often that it becomes an obsession and an uncontrollable habit, generally associated with a particular type of fear. It could be compared to the insurance salesman who can start with any given remark in any conversation and wind up three minutes later with conclusive proof that you should therefore take out additional insurance.

A fairly typical illustration of psychasthenia is the case of Martha W., a college student who first demonstrated her neurosis as the outgrowth of a laboratory experiment. Martha was chosen at random in class, and instructed to wash her hands thoroughly with soap and water. When she had finished, she dipped a finger into sterile water, and dropped the water into a culture which was placed away for forty-eight hours and then examined in class. Purpose of the experiment was to illustrate the types of germs that may still remain on the hands after ordinary washing. But, for Martha, the experiment produced unexpected results. She gazed in horror through a microscope. She became ill and had to be excused from class as an effort was made to estimate the number and types of germs in the culture. She commenced washing her hands incessantly, refusing to touch doorknobs or to handle money, and within a surprisingly few days she had to be sent home from school.

She was a highly intelligent girl. But it did no good to explain to her that she had survived for nineteen years, while touching doorknobs and other things equally germ-laden; or to point out that millions of people manage to survive in this unhygienic world with but the barest conception of sanitation.

She knew all those things and had argued them to herself long before her visit to my office. But still she couldn't force herself to reach out with her bare hand and grasp a doorknob. She could be compared to the more familiar type of person who methodically dreams up a dozen reasons why he should quit smoking, shudders twice, and then lights up another cigarette.

Martha's parents, incidentally, were extremely bitter about the whole thing, and considered filing suit against the school, convinced that their daughter's condition had been brought on solely by the laboratory experiment. "After all, Doctor, she was perfectly normal up till then."

But in that, of course, her parents were mistaken—as they later came to realize. A perfectly normal person would hardly present such a violent reaction to a routine laboratory experiment. In effect, Martha's emotional status on that day in class could be compared to the accident that's just waiting for a chance to happen.

Actually, it developed, Martha had been tormented for some time by an overwhelming sense of guilt because of an earlier sexual transgression, and the guilt had been reënforced with fear after attending a lecture on the subject of venereal infection. But these things she had discussed with no one. Unconsciously, she had grasped at the sudden and overwhelming fear of all germs as a chance to change her mental diet, almost as a patient in a dental chair will resolutely try to think about last summer's vacation rather than thinking about the dentist's drill that is dangling like the sword of Damocles over his head. It is a process of substitution.

From a psychological standpoint, the hand-washing routine is particularly interesting for it undoubtedly ties up with a subconscious wish to wash the sins away, and it shows up strikingly often in the obsessive-compulsive personality.

Life in a modern society brings an inevitable host of conflicts. And in each case the organism attempts to adjust itself for the greatest amount of comfort or satisfaction possible.

If the emotional conflict is great, it may leave the individual in a state bordering on exhaustion, like a shadow-boxer who has all but knocked himself out in the twenty-fifth round. This condition, when it has progressed beyond the outer bounds of normality, is known as neurasthenia, or the so-called fatigue neurosis.

Barbara R., a frail young lady twenty-six years of age, complained of such complete exhaustion that she had to remain in bed. Two older brothers had previously died of tuberculosis and despite the negative findings of physicians, Barbara and her family clung to the belief that the girl was tubercular. She was brought to the hospital when she complained of almost unbearable pain in her right arm, and was transferred to the psychopathic ward for observation after examinations had once again revealed no discernible pathological factors.

The family history was negative, but it was apparent that the situation within the home was not a happy one. The father was a partial invalid as the result of an accident, and the family had lived for years in poverty.

There were many contributing factors, but investigation revealed that Barbara's basic conflict was the old familiar one, between a desire to leave home and live her own life, and a sense of duty which tied her down as the breadwinner of the family. Her fear of tuberculosis was morbid, and was complicated by the fact that her two older brothers had both died in their twenty-sixth year, and the conviction that she would follow.

It is interesting to note that as a child, Barbara had fallen from a tree and broken her right arm, and it had been clumsily attended by an inefficient practitioner. As is so strikingly common in such cases, the subconscious mind chose to enact a role of suffering in which it had acquired experience, rather than tackling an entirely new role. Thus, Barbara complained of the excruciating pain in her right arm, rather than in her left leg, for example. Just as Mrs. G., mentioned earlier, dramatized her four o'clock conflicts with attacks of asthma— a type of suffering in which she'd had previous experience.

When Barbara came to understand the nature of her conflicts and the reason for her fatigue, she showed evidence of improvement. Through the coöperation of a welfare agency, arrangements were made for the care of the mother and the father while Barbara secured a job in town, shared an apartment with another girl, and sent home such money as she could reasonably afford, thus resolving the basic conflict.

It is foolish to assume that Barbara was merely pretending to feel pain at the time when she was admitted to the hospital. To her, beyond the shadow of a doubt, the pain was real and the suffering was genuine. No real understanding of neuroses can be achieved by the person who holds dogmatically to the conviction: "Aw, he's just putting on an act to get sympathy." The person who can pretend to suffer while actually feeling no pain may be abnormal but is certainly not neurotic. Even a reasonably normal individual who professes a splitting headache in order to break a date, may find himself gulping aspirin tablets before the evening is over, and when the time for pretending is past.

A football player can have his nose broken during the course of a game and hardly realize it until later. But if it commences to heal improperly and must be rebroken in the doctor's office, the same rugged hero of the gridiron may die a thousand deaths in the physician's waiting room, in grim anticipation of the calamity. Anticipation is the magnifying glass of the emotions. And the boxer being mauled within the prize ring may be less conscious of pain than is the man sitting at home on the rim of the bathtub, cautiously prying a length of adhesive tape from a hairy calf.

Pain, itself, is a perception—with a highly portable threshold. If it is true that a person under anaesthesia feels no pain, then it is equally true that the neurotic feels the pains of which he complains, even though no pathological symptoms can be found.

The threshold of pain moves in and out, like a plush carpet at the Ritz. And in the final analysis, the only real authority on whether a given individual is perceiving pain, is the person who's yelling ouch. The psychologist, in his most brilliant moment, can do little more than determine whether or not the perception is normal. A man on a humid and sizzling day in the tropics may suffer alternating chills and fever, and no emphatic quoting of the weather report is going to talk him out of his chills. He is more of an authority on what he feels, than is the most reliable Fahrenheit thermometer.

One of the nastiest tricks ever hatched up by the office wit, is to arrange for three or four different persons to question the health of a selected victim: "You feeling all right today, Joe? You look awful . . . just like my uncle looked a half hour before he died of heart failure." If subtly handled, poor old Joe may be home in bed and gasping out the terms of his will by two o'clock in the afternoon. And his suffering is genuine.

Some persons, of course, are more subject to suggestion than are others; more easily stampeded. When they go to pieces too easily or too completely they are abnormal, and their behavior is highly erratic. This abnormality is the oldest known of the mental disorders. Even the Greeks had a word for it, and the word meant "uterus." For back in those rugged days it was considered an affliction peculiar to the female of the species. Out of respect to their early diagnosis, we still use the old Greek term, although it's been flattened out a bit through the process of translation into English. We know it as "hysteria," and under that broad heading are grouped a host of peculiar neurotic phenomena.

I had encountered cases of hysteria during my early association with Dr. Morton Prince; during my studies in Vienna, Zurich, Paris and Leipzig, and off-and-on during my years of practice in Los Angeles. But not until 1918 and the days of World War I did I get into the wholesale end of the business.

Because of the urgent need for trained psychiatrists, I was offered a commission as captain in the United States Army and instructed to report at Palo Alto, California. And there, with hardly more than a handshake and a pat on the back, I was immediately placed in charge of a ward . . . and promptly forgotten.

For nearly four months I seethed with disillusionment and dissatisfaction, for I'd somehow envisioned a military career as something more exciting than my routine chores of nearly two decades. Geographically, I had advanced about four hundred miles up the map; while financially I'd progressed approximately the same distance downward. And so in June of 1918 I went to my commanding officer and explained the situation, and requested an opportunity to attend officer training school.

"After all," I protested, "if I'm going to wear the uniform, I ought to know something about it. Which hand to salute with, and that sort of thing. Nobody has told me a blessed thing." And it was, in fact, rather embarrassing. I had picked up my tips on military behavior on a catch-as-catch-can basis; and I'd learned the ratings of shoulder bars and eagles and oak leaves somewhat like a novice learning poker.

I discovered then that the commanding officer was no better off than I was. And so we shipped out together.

My four months of observing military etiquette out of the corner of the eye, stood me in good stead when I reached Fort Riley, Kansas. And almost before I realized it, I was placed in charge of a company made up entirely of medical men. In the long history of the United States Army, I doubt if it has ever witnessed a more incongruous conglomeration of awkward but willing recruits—white-haired doughboys puffing like locomotives—world-renowned surgeons who could name every muscle and bone and fiber of the body, but who somehow couldn't remember which was the right or left foot—men who could handle a scalpel with enviable finesse, but who couldn't adjust a bayonet any more proficiently than a cub bear handling a pop bottle. To make it particularly embarrassing, many of the men struggling awkwardly but willingly to obey my commands were men far more prominent than I ever hoped to be.

Somehow we survived it. And eventually I found myself a casual, attached to a base hospital at Commercy, Alsace-Lorraine. The hospital was a mammoth affair, and for some reason which has never been explained to me to this day, I discovered that regulations required my signature on the card of every patient admitted. This was a time-consuming affair, particularly in view of the fact that each signature had to be preceded by an interview of the patient, whether he was brought in with shrapnel wounds or frostbite. And since I was the only psychiatrist attached to the hospital, my remaining time had to be devoted to those men in need of psychiatric attention.

A certain amount of belated ridicule has been heaped upon those of us who classified so many different cases of hysteria under the convenient heading of shell shock. But there is no particular reason for ridicule or contempt. Each neurosis is in itself an individual malady. Whether fifty thousand cases are listed together under a single all-inclusive title, or whether an attempt is made to separate them according to type into smaller groups under individual headings, it is, in the final analysis, largely a matter of bookkeeping. The term shell shock served quite adequately at the time.

There is no particular reason to separate the vegetarians from the meat-eaters; those who prefer light meat from those who prefer dark meat—when you have nothing to serve but K-rations. And it would have been little more than a waste of time during World War I, methodically to separate the hysterics according to type—and then offer them all the same limited therapy, which was the only thing available.

There was an endless stream of shell shock victims moving back from the front-line trenches. And behind nearly every case was a fairly standard story: Grief. Disillusionment. No mail from home. Fear. And the everlasting rain. Hysteria is sudden in its appearance, but it is generally preceded by a gradual sinking of morale.

They were a pitiful legion. Some blind. Some deaf. Some paralyzed in arms or legs. Some emotionally wound up and screaming, and others blank and vacant and whimpering. They were all the more pitiful because they were misunderstood, not only by their buddies but too often by the nurses and physicians and officers and chaplains, and all the folks back home.

There was little we could offer them: Hydrotherapy, to relax taut nerves and muscles. Visits from the chaplain. Reassuring words. Sedatives and prolonged sleep. And that was about all.

The acknowledgment that these men had nothing organically wrong led to widespread misunderstanding. A hard-bitten infantry officer informed me that in his honest opinion there were no such things as hysteria or shell shock. "Those men are gold bricks, every damn' one of them. The more you pamper them, the more they increase in number. If I had my way, I'd turn a fire hose on 'em and snap 'em out of it, and then send 'em back to the front lines. Inside a week, I'll bet you wouldn't have any more cases of shell shock!"

Similar sentiments, in more cautious terms, were being expressed by some within the medical profession. And the disconcerting part of it all was the possibility that they had a point. For hysteria, like vomiting, can be suggestive and sympathetic. Basically it is an escape mechanism; and even in a burning building, fewer will seek the fire escape if those who reach it are turned back, badly burned.

Also, there are pretenders to every title—even that of "Neurotic." And beyond a doubt there were men sent back from the fighting lines whose odd behavior was deliberate and deceptive.

But the true hysteric is not consciously attempting to fool anyone. Unconsciously, however, he is attempting to fool everyone, including himself. Here again it's the subconscious mind that's taken the situation in hand. The Chief Operator is unimpressed by top sergeants, brass bands, and the Articles of War. She recognizes only one responsibility and that's toward the stockholders of her own particular corporation—the multitude of cells that have thrown in their lot together, to make up the mind and the body of the one individual involved. She's short-circuited her switchboard in an attempt to find escape from a situation that has become a little too uncomfortable. She's quit taking orders from the conscious mind, having reluctantly reached a major decision: "The big boss in the front office must be off his trolley, or he wouldn't deliberately keep us out here when the bullets are flying."

A neurosis, in effect, is a form of mental mutiny. Or an automatic pop-off valve to relieve the pressure of internal conflict. We think of it, ordinarily, as a sign of emotional weakness. There are just as valid reasons, in my opinion, to think of it as an indication of emotional strength. In the eternal struggle to find comfort and satisfaction in the brief period of a single lifetime, the neurotic may find escape from an unpleasant situation while the more normal person remains behind to face the music. It's all in how you look at it.

Psychology is based largely on the premise that an organism will seek those situations which yield satisfaction and will seek to avoid those situations which yield dissatisfaction. This underlies the behavior pattern of everything from sunflowers and morning glories to diplomats and flagpole-sitters. And there's considerable evidence that a neurosis is a natural by-product of this entirely logical attitude.

The child, at an early age, learns that he can gain sympathy and attention through illness; have ice cream for dessert and be excused from school. And if the sudden solicitude makes life more pleasant for him than is his customary lot—and if he observes the technique being cunningly used by older members of the family—he has commenced his primary training in the care and cultivation of a neurosis. He has observed a simple lesson in achieving satisfaction.

He may learn also that he can gain parental attention or other satisfying rewards through the process of the temper tantrum. He may discover that he can avoid punishment for his misdeeds by disavowing responsibility: "Honest, Mama, I didn't go to walk in the flower bed. Willie pushed me." He may discover, quite casually, that he doesn't have to wear his frilly shirt to Sunday school if he conveniently forgets to put it into the dirty clothes hamper after it's become soiled. And he may find peculiar satisfaction in ascribing his own shortcomings to others: "Well, if I'm a liar, you're another! And you're even worser!"

These are all simple primary lessons and the child weighs them thoughtfully in his conscious mind. He knows pretty well what he's doing, and precisely why he's doing it. But the process is being dutifully observed by the subconscious mind. Basic habits of reaction are being started which may grow through the years. And each, upon reaching full bloom, may qualify as a definite indication of neurosis.

The adult neurotic, while still deriving a certain morbid satisfaction from the attention gained through illness, has no conscious knowledge of any satisfaction. There is no recognized pretense. With tears of absolute sincerity, he may insist that he'd give everything he owns for just one good night's sleep, free from his eternal suffering. He means it, too—every word of it—so far as his conscious mind is concerned. But the Chief Operator of the subconscious is listening in on the entire conversation and practically purring with inward satisfaction as she hears the sympathetic words of Mrs. Murphy tendered over the back fence: "Oh, you poor man, you!" And just to make the demonstration convincing, the Chief Operator possibly flips a few strategic switches, causing the entire body to quiver like a Model-T Ford with open throttle.

The explosive tirades of temper by the neurotic may also be beyond the power of the conscious mind to keep in check. And there's little it can do except to apologize later: "I don't know what made me blow up that way. I just sort of went to pieces."

A highly significant pattern of convenience may be found in the neurotic's amnesia—in the things he forgets, is totally unable to remember even when he tries—and in the little acts of unconscious behavior: "Look what just came in the mail, Martha! I sent your brother the ten bucks I owed him, and then I absent-mindedly addressed the envelope to myself!"

The shifting of blame by the adult is particularly revealing. He no longer uses such a simple explanation as "Willie pushed me." But he may offer more subtle or more elaborate explanations, sometimes enacted in pantomime instead of being expressed in words. The football player who has just let a long pass slip through his fingers may make a fairly conspicuous gesture of wiping his hands upon his jersey, thus explaining to everybody in the stadium that his fingers were slippery from perspiration. The baseball player who's just muffled a sizzling grounder may cautiously slip back to pick up a tiny rock at the scene of his error, to illustrate why the ball took a bad hop. And Mama, when she serves a charcoal-coated meatloaf, may unleash a verbal tirade, on the theory that a good offense is the best defense: "Henry, you've simply got to get a man from the gas company to come out and check the temperature controls on that oven. I've stood it as long as I can!"

The neurotic individual may go a step beyond. I remember interviewing a young lady who told me during her visit, "Everybody at the office where I work is against me, and has been, ever since I first started to work there. They're all the time talking about me behind my back, and making fun of me. I can tell by the way they act when I first come into a room." She told me she had worked for three years in the same office, but when I asked if she had received any raises in pay or any promotions she nearly exploded: "How could I get any promotions, when everybody blames me for everything that goes wrong?" Later, the same young lady came to realize that she had been a very inefficient worker and a very undependable and disloyal employee. But she'd found it easier to blame others than honestly to face her own shortcomings.

A more advanced neurotic—a man—once told me in all earnestness that he was unable to concentrate on his work because of the radio waves passing through his body. "Only one place I ever go that I really feel good, and that's at my uncle's place. He lives way back up in the mountains, where they don't get any radio reception of any kind. Just the minute I get there, I start feeling better."

He conceded, during the course of our discussion, that it was maybe in his mind. "I suppose it's silly, Doc. But can a man help how he feels? Whether it's in my mind or not, it's driving me nuts. I can't concentrate." His occupation was that of accountant, a task in which a certain amount of concentration is essential . . . and where a lack of an ability to concentrate would be a logical excuse for any errors, failures, or oversights.

The fully arrived psychotic, on the other hand, will hardly concede that the trouble is in his mind. "I've got worms crawling all around inside my fingers," he announces emphatically. You can read him three volumes on the subject of anatomy, present the statements of authorities proving that the situation he describes is impossible, and show him his hands under the fluoroscope. And his only comment may be, "But you see, Doc, I've got these worms crawling around inside my fingers."

Underneath it all, from the perfectly normal individual to the advanced psychotic, may be found the simple groping for comfort and satisfaction—a struggle to avoid that dismal situation wherein the individual admits responsibility for his shortcomings. They are increasingly elaborate variations of the simple disclaimer: "Willie pushed me."

The struggle for social approval and the striving for self-esteem are largely competitive affairs. And the desire to push one's self ahead may be paralleled by a less gracious desire to hold the others back, and particularly to trip the leaders. Our own shortcomings somehow seem more tolerable if we can recognize similar and even greater shortcomings in those about us. And we become least tolerant of those failings in others which we have refused to recognize in ourselves.

Often it's the town drunkard who spreads the malicious little stories about seeing the minister sneak into the back door of the saloon. And it's the town gossip who becomes indignant about the minister's wife spreading malicious slander. Much can be learned about the individual's unconscious appraisal of himself, through the study of his particular pattern of intolerance toward the shortcomings of others.

This process, known as projection, is the ultimate outgrowth of the youthful protest: "If I'm a liar, you're another! And you're even worser!" It's the individual's attempt to bolster his own self-esteem by pushing down on the opposite end of the teeter-totter of comparison. In the neurotic individual it grows into a zealousness for magnifying those faults in others which he has stubbornly refused to recognize in his own self-appraisal.

Somewhere behind every neurosis can be found the unfailing pattern of convenience. And it is the contention of many authorities that a short cut may often be found in seeking the cause in any particular case: Merely study the odd neurotic behavior of the individual, and then figure out what he or she could gain from such behavior. Personally, I have never had too much success with attempted short cuts because of the complexities of the psychic process. But the theory is no doubt sound.

Highly significant in the study of neuroses is the part played by the individual's relationship to the society in which he lives.

Certain primitive and not-so-primitive people show little compassion for those who are weak or ill. Theirs is a hard-bitten philosophy, comparable to drowning the runt of the litter. In such a society, how could the individual derive any satisfaction from professing illness? When he meets with contempt instead of sympathy, what pleasure could he find in advertising his weakness? And significantly, many of the miseries which infest our Western civilization are here practically unknown. The ability of primitive men and women to withstand pain, and to survive the rigors of a rugged life without complaint, is something awesome to behold.

And it all points to the eventual assumption that neuroses are a by-product of social contact, progressing in step with the advancement of civilization. There are no beggars where there is no charity. And apparently there are no neurotics where there is nothing to be gained by neurosis.

# 12

*The excesses of our youth are drafts upon our old age,*
*payable with interest about thirty years after date.*

—COLTON

FEW THINGS IN this world are more magnificent to behold or more disillusioning to read than the typical written guarantee with its heavily embossed seal and its cautious references to "defects of material and workmanship."

A number of years ago I purchased a set of automobile tires that bore an absolute, unconditional guarantee. "Don't make any difference what it is," the salesman assured me enthusiastically, "if you don't get twenty thousand miles from those tires just bring 'em in and I'll give you a whole new set absolutely free."

It so happened that one of the tires went to pieces before it had gone five thousand miles and I returned confidently to the place where I'd bought it.

"You musta hit a rock, or run over a chuckhole in the road or something," the man announced sadly, examining the defunct tire. "See where these cords are all torn loose, sideways? Won't anything cause a break like that, except you hit a road hazard." And I learned to my sorrow that my absolute, unconditional guarantee didn't cover such things as hitting rocks or chuckholes, developing punctures, contacting road hazards, or driving on the flat tire long enough to bring the car to a halt.

"After all," the man gasped in amazement at my stupidity, "you wouldn't expect that we could guarantee a new tire against anything that could happen to it. Why, you could go home and chop it to pieces with an axe when the tread started to wear a little thin, and then expect us to give you a brand-new tire."

I conceded that he had a point there, and in a burst of confidence he explained to me, "I'll tell you how it is, Doctor. You maybe didn't give this tire the best care you could have given it. It's been treated kind of rough. At the same time, maybe the tire wasn't quite as good as it could of been. I don't mean it was defective, you understand . . . but out of a carload of tires there's bound to be one that's not quite as good as some of the rest. Just so there won't be any hard feelings, I'm going to give you a new tire exactly at cost. I won't make a nickel on it."

You don't have to be a tire merchant to understand that viewpoint. You can also be a psychiatrist. For psychiatrists, too, face the identical problem in attempting to trace the cause of a psychosis. Sometimes it's impossible to tell just how much of the failure is due to defective material and workmanship, and how much is due to road hazards. Only we refer to them as heredity and environment.

It is practically impossible to determine how much of the tendency toward the abnormal was inherent in the individual, and how much of it was acquired from the bumps and bruises along the highway of life. And we can do little more than accept the magnanimous philosophy of the tire merchant, conceding that it's maybe a little of both.

A courageous and commendable effort has been made down through the years to divide all psychoses into two general classifications: organic psychoses, which are known to have an organic basis; and functional psychoses which include all the rest.

It was a logical place to attempt a division of the whole wide world of psychoses into respective hemispheres. And undoubtedly it seemed like a good idea at the time.

Obviously, if a man sips a fifth of gin, uses narcotics, or lands on his cranium after a fall from a peach tree, and then behaves in a peculiar fashion, he is hardly to be considered in the same fix as the man who develops his peculiarities without such obvious assistance.

Under the banner of organic psychoses have been grouped those abnormalities which have tangible roots that might conceivably be weighed upon scales, analyzed under a microscope, or precisely fitted into the known laws of heredity. These include abnormalities arising from disease, glandular disorder, accident, toxic infection, the use of alcohol, opiates, and so on.

Functional psychoses are the ones that can't be so easily explained by a bump on the head, a spot on the liver, or an empty bottle in the cupboard.

Being bluntly unscientific about it all, we might roughly conclude that the organic psychoses have tangible physical causes, while the functional psychoses have intangible mental causes. But we must remember, in the same breath, that this boundary was surveyed and marked off in an era prior to the introduction of the psychosomatic premise. It was a division dreamed up by man for his own convenience in setting up a filing system. And there's no remote indication that it has ever been recognized by Nature.

I remember quite vividly the first time in my life I ever beheld an international boundary. It was during a summer vacation when I was in high school, and I went with the family on an extended trip up into Maine. We rode one day to the Canadian border—a cleared strip through the forest. I'm not sure now just what I expected to find. Possibly I'd taken for granted that Canada would be a different color from the United States, as it was on the large map at school. But I remember sitting for a long time in amazement at a remarkable discovery.

"Why, the grass and the trees and the earth and everything all look the same on the other side," I protested, and there came a chorus of derision from my older brothers and sisters.

"Look at the birds," I persisted. "They just fly across as if there weren't any boundary there. They don't even know the difference!"

"What did you expect them to do, take out a passport?" one of my brothers asked in disgust. But my father placed a hand upon my shoulder in a gesture of reassurance.

"When God made the earth," he told me, "He didn't mark it off into sections. He didn't build fences, or boundaries. He made all of the earth for all of His people. Men have made all the boundaries, and all of the boundaries are artificial. I'm quite sure God doesn't recognize them, any more than do the birds."

And as time has gone on, it seems to me, many of our man-made boundaries have become untenable. The more we learn in this world, the more difficult it becomes to cling to the convenient little dividing lines of the past—geographic, social, or scientific.

It was reasonably simple for our forefathers to divide all living organisms into two groups: plants and animals. Practically anybody could tell the difference between a hippopotamus and a rutabaga, just at a casual glance. But with the invention of the microscope and the discovery of microscopic organisms it has become increasingly difficult to trace the line of demarcation. And science, to this day, has reserved judgment on certain unicellular organisms, unwilling to classify them definitely and exclusively under either heading.

It was comparatively simple during the eons of geographic isolation to distinguish between the various races of men. But with increased social intercourse and racial intermarriage there come new problems and a multi-racial no-man's-land.

Even the once-popular division of athletes into their respective classes of amateurs and professionals becomes a hopeless puzzle as the line of demarcation falls across the college gridiron.

And likewise as we gradually learn a little more about the psychosomatic entity of man, we find it increasingly difficult to follow the old boundaries that separated the mental from the physical; the functional from the organic.

When a man has sipped a fifth of gin and embarked upon an erratic behavior pattern, it's a simple matter to insist that the cause of his strange behavior is something very tangible and easily understandable, and generally sold in bottles. But there remains the parallel question of what drove him to drink in the first place? And here we run into matters that are social, mental, and emotional, and altogether elusive— and the presence of which cannot be detected by asking the gentleman to walk a chalkline or pick up pennies from the sidewalk.

Whether an individual is normal or abnormal, an alcoholic or a schizophrenic, there is every logical reason to believe that he is the net result of his entire human experience plus definite hereditary factors. And it is perhaps futile to attempt to isolate any single cause, to hold it up to the light of recognition, and to explain smugly: "Here's the villain of the plot. This, and this alone, explains why you are what you are." It can be only a partial explanation at best.

Many different men, pursuing many different studies, have produced many different explanations of why and how a functional neurosis develops. It's due to heredity. It's due to body type and structure. It's due to glandular disturbance. It's due to social environment. It's due to focal infection. It's due to physiological changes within the body. It's due to psychic disturbances. And since many of these explanations have come from sincere and highly respected men, and since each found sufficient evidence to convince himself and to convince others, the only decent and broad-minded thing to do is to accept the bulk of them as being essentially correct. For many of those things are enmeshed and intertwined in every case history. And the world as yet has produced no man of sufficient genius to unravel all the threads of our complex lives, and to determine just what parts of the warp and the woof give the world its lunatic fringe.

At one time a number of years ago a young man who was a friend of the family stopped by our house on his wedding trip and introduced us to his young and very charming bride. And as it was late in the afternoon my wife insisted that they remain for dinner. There was a certain amount of mild protest, but she insisted.

The following day came horrifying news: Our young friends had been driving across a small bridge the night before when a gasoline truck had sideswiped the car ahead of them, crashed into a bridge abutment, and burned. The young man had apparently been killed almost instantly as his car plowed into the truck which was sprawled across the highway, and his young bride, severely burned, had died on the way to the hospital.

"Oh my God!" my wife shrieked as she heard the news. "If I hadn't insisted that they stay for dinner, they would have been miles past there when the accident happened!" She blamed herself bitterly, and it was a difficult task to make her calm down.

A few days later after the funeral in San Diego, I sat talking to the young man's distraught father.

"They were going to take the train north," he told me sadly. "They had all the arrangements made. But then I decided to let them take my car." He sat in abject misery.

"I can't help thinking, if I'd just let them go ahead with their plans, they'd both be alive and well today."

At approximately the same time, the young man's sister, in another part of the house, was explaining the irony of it to my wife:

"Actually," she said, "they didn't plan to be married until the latter part of June. That's when Paul was supposed to get his vacation. But one of the men down at the office wanted to trade with him because he couldn't get reservations at some resort until later. So Paul traded with him, and they changed all their plans in a terrible hurry. If it hadn't been for that, this never would have happened."

There were, I suppose, many other "ifs" that never came to my attention. If the young man hadn't traded vacations, if he hadn't driven a car instead of taking the train, if he hadn't remained at our house for dinner, and if a thousand other things hadn't worked out exactly as they did, he surely wouldn't have been crossing a small bridge at the precise instant when a gasoline truck skidded, hit the abutment, and burned.

And similar imponderables may be found in infinite number, in tracing the case history of any psychotic: If he hadn't been ridiculed so much as a child, he wouldn't have been so shy. If he hadn't been so shy, he wouldn't have spent so much time by himself. If he hadn't spent so much time by himself, he wouldn't have indulged so much in masturbation. If he hadn't felt guilty because of masturbation, he wouldn't have cultivated his habits of reference and projection, his delusions and hallucinations; his internal organs would have operated in different ratio, and body chemistry would not have reached an abnormal balance. There can be a thousand "ifs" when the story is stretched out fine enough, and the change of a single one of them could alter the plot from that point on out.

So which is the villain? Ridicule? Shyness? Social isolation? Masturbation? A feeling of guilt? Glandular disturbance? You can pick out any one at random. And whichever you choose, it's an odds-on chance that you won't be entirely wrong, and can't be entirely correct. You can't dramatize the entire plot, with just one member from the cast.

Three things, however, show up with monotonous regularity in the psychotic background: sex, religion, or feelings of insecurity. It is possible, I'm reasonably sure, for a psychosis to develop with none of these in the cast, just as it is possible to arrange an amateur entertainment without an accordion solo. It is possible—but highly improbable.

In my opinion, it will never be possible for the home diagnostician to recognize and distinguish between the various psychoses, with anything resembling reasonable accuracy except in the most advanced and typical of cases. It is a sufficiently ambitious dream at the moment to hope that the technique may some day be mastered by the better trained of the psychiatrists. For there is considerable overlapping. And as in every other cataloguing system, the section marked Miscellaneous tends to become the most crowded.

Schizophrenia (once commonly known as dementia praecox) is the most common and most familiar of the major psychoses, contributing to the confinement of upward of forty to forty-five percent of the patients spending any considerable length of time in mental institutions.

The typical advanced schizophrenic may be quite readily identified by his emotional blunting—his vacant-eyed stare—his isolation inside a social vacuum, and his general indifference toward environmental influence which would ordinarily be expected to produce emotional response. Schizophrenic patients, for example, often show no regret and no apparent reaction of any kind, upon being committed to a hospital. They've reached a point of I-don't-know or I-don't-care.

But diagnosis of schizophrenia at this point is little more than a psychic post-mortem. The malady develops slowly and insidiously through months or years. And quite often, in its earlier stages, it may resemble other psychoses and be confused with them, by any self-styled amateur diagnostician.

From the observance of approximately nine hundred cases of schizophrenia through my years of practice, plus such training as I have received and such study as I have made, certain conclusions are to me inescapable. Almost inevitably, a feeling of personal failure can be found in the background of the patient. Without benefit of trial by jury, he has weighed himself and found himself wanting.

The causes of this may be many and varied, as has been suggested. And it is futile to seek an isolated villain in the plot. From his parents, from his friends, from his reading and study, and possibly from his daydreams, he has formed a definite picture of the type of individual he should be. And from disheartening introspection, he has concluded that he has definitely missed the boat.

He wants to be his hero-ideal—clean, wholesome, courageous, honest, trustworthy, handsome, prosperous, intelligent, etc., etc., etc. But in frank self-appraisal he finds himself continuing to masturbate on occasion, despite his good resolutions. He finds himself walking three blocks out of his way to avoid the little yapping fox terrier that fills his soul with terror. He stares in the mirror and finds his skin marked with acne, and he recalls some whispered comment about this being the result of masturbation. He checks over the achievements of his life to date and finds them strangely lacking, and he contrasts this to Papa's proud story about earning his way in the world at twelve years of age. For these, or for any other similar or dissimilar reasons, he loses a large measure of self-respect.

There are undoubtedly thousands who reach this point and who—for some reason or other—get steered upon a different pathway. It possibly may take no more than a chance change of environment, the companionship of some new-found and understanding friend, or possibly no more than a well-timed pat on the back. But this is sheer speculation. For those who find the different pathway do not provide the future case histories where psychiatrists and statisticians grub for facts.

Of those who continue on toward ultimate schizophrenia, the pathway also divides. There are those who, having lost their self-respect and having consciously or subconsciously accepted their verdict of personal failure, continue merely to drift. They make no attempted resistance. They do not fight. There is no effort to turn over a new leaf, but merely a resignation to the inevitable. "I am what I am, and it's a damn' shame; but that's what I am, regardless." The individual may withdraw to a world of fantasy, and possibly hasten the process by resorting to drink or to drugs. The listlessness and the apathy grow, and the patient finds himself in a mental hospital with no marked hallucinations and no particularly bizarre ideas. He has merely drifted down toward dissolution and destruction along the pathway of no resistance. He is the type of individual who's apt to leave the neighbors bewildered and confused:

"It's a funny thing. He never really went crazy. Just sort of got quiet and thoughtful. Hit the bottle pretty regular. And then they locked him up. But he never really acted crazy, any way that I could see."

There are others who refuse to drift. They struggle to "save face," and resort to distortion. In an attempt to justify their self-admitted personal failure, they fall back on the "Willie-pushed-me" technique— become sensitive and suspicious, and heap all of the blame upon others. They interpret the most commonplace things of the workaday world as being part of a vast plot. Hallucinations of hearing are common; visual hallucinations and hallucinations of taste and smell less common but not unusual. Strange and sometimes violent acts may be performed in response to these hallucinations. "Jesus spoke to me, and He told me to set fire to that house, which is the home of infidels."

Such persons are frequently removed to mental hospitals before the final curtain of emotional isolation has descended. The neighbors, generally, are not so confused. "I tell you, that guy was crazier than a hoot owl! Why, I was afraid to even let the children outside the house, until they had him locked up." But inversely, because the symptoms were dramatic and the confinement earlier arranged, the patient may have a better chance for recovery under the recent achieve-ments in psychotherapy.

Eric V., apparently, was the drifting type. He was thirty-three years old when first examined, and already an advanced schizophrenic. His mother, still living at the time of his commitment, was an apparently neurotic woman, nervous and quick-tempered, and inclined to blame others for all difficulties. He had come to this country from Germany when seven years old, and just shortly prior to American active par-ticipation in World War I. Eric had been taunted and tormented by other children at school because of his German parentage, and denied acceptance by his own generation. As a child, Eric was described as obedient, quiet, and conscientious—not given to a display of emotions of any kind, even when tormented. After graduation from high school he entered college and took up the study of medicine. Here he was considered an excellent student, but because of financial reasons he was never able to attend for more than one or two quarters, before dropping out to earn more money. At twenty-nine years of age and having not yet completed his fourth year of medical study, he gave up the attempt.

He worked only spasmodically during the following years, lost confidence in himself, and entertained the conviction that people were universally aligned against him because of his German parentage. He became gradually more depressed and more seclusive.

At the time when he was committed he had not worked for several months, and had spent nearly all of the time locked up in his room. At the hospital he was quiet and depressed. He would answer questions only in monosyllables, refused to accept any work assignments, and gradually became more and more withdrawn. Most of his waking hours were spent quietly staring out the window; and occasionally, for no apparent reason, he would laugh. Both insulin and electro-shock therapies were tried without improvement.

Feelings of guilt, failure, and rejection lay heavily across his back-ground. It is reasonable to assume that fear and hatred smouldered there also, as a result of the tormenting at school and the lack of understanding at home. And those who keep the statistics on World

War I, could no doubt add one more digit to the casualty list of that great conflict, to include the record of Eric V.

In rather sharp contrast is the case of Thelma G., who also had feelings of personal failure but who refused to part with her self-respect without a struggle. She was twenty-five years of age at the time of commitment, a college graduate of good habits and high intelligence. However, she had been consistently unable to adjust well or to hold a job. Even in her college days she had been seclusive, and demonstrated the conviction that she was being picked on consistently by students and faculty members. She had in recent years developed a conviction that her food was being poisoned as part of a plot against her, and her undernourished body showed the result of long and frequent fasts. There was no sexual experience in her background, but she frequently charged that others were attempting to infect her with venereal disease. She had auditory hallucinations which she considered to be a type of telepathy, and even after her commitment she charged that doctors, attendants and other patients were attempting to influence her in a sexual way through telepathic means.

Although those close to her had known for many years that Thelma G. was "odd," there had been no previous attempt to seek psychiatric aid or diagnosis and the case had progressed inexcusably far. However, the vacuum of isolation hadn't yet surrounded her. She showed emotional reaction to commitment, and to her hallucinations. She was capable of intelligent conversation on many topics and she entered the work-therapy program with reasonable cooperation. Insulin and electro-shock therapies showed only transient improvement, and Thelma G. was still in the hospital at the time of my last contact with the case, and essentially the same as she had been at the time of admission. But there remained for her the hope of eventual improvement.

Had Thelma G. allowed herself to drift—if she had not struggled to regain her self-respect by attempting to place all the blame for her failings upon others—if she had not developed her delusions and her hallucinations, and if she had not given voice to her bitter and fantastic accusations—then she undoubtedly would have been allowed to sit in self-imposed isolation until the vacuum had become complete, and she would have received her first psychiatric attention at a time when she had become an unresponsive chunk of human clay, staring uncomprehendingly into space.

Thelma, incidentally, was the daughter of a reasonably well-to-do family. It is entirely unlikely that any apparent physical abnormality would have been allowed to continue for two weeks without a competent medical examination. But a so-called mental abnormality was allowed to go unattended for many years under the hopeful philosophy, "Maybe if we don't pay any attention to it, it will go away." And the entire family paid the price in full for that prejudice which prohibits a prompt psychiatric examination.

There are, of course, other boundaries—within boundaries. Having divided psychoses into the organic and the functional, and having separated the functional psychoses into respective maladies of which schizophrenia is only one, there remained the task of dividing schizophrenia into types. And thus the case of Eric V. is known as the simple type, and the case of Thelma G. is known as the paranoid type of schizophrenia. (There are also other types.)

For these and other reasons which could be quoted at length and almost indefinitely, it seems quite unlikely that even the more enlightened layman will be able to diagnose accurately the mental abnormalities of those around him, and much less likely that he could diagnose his own. Being mentally abnormal and being personally involved, do not contribute to impartial diagnosis.

Fortunately, however, the precise name and type of the abnormality are matters of academic interest only. It should be sufficient for the enlightened layman to gain a general knowledge of the approximate boundaries of that fog-beclouded no-man's-land where normality ends and abnormality begins.

And that is no modest assignment in itself.

# 13

*Everything that exceeds the bounds of moderation, has an unstable foundation.*—SENECA

ONE OF THE most disillusioning things about being a psychiatrist is the fact that sooner or later you must part with a lot of cherished little notions about social justice. You must survey evidence with an impartial attitude and learn not to question the wisdom of Him who dictates the plot.

I have envied writers of fiction who can study their characters and then hand out fictional destinies with a high regard for things as they should be—eliminate a malady or bring the departed back from the grave with one bold stroke of the pen. I have sometimes criticized but always coveted the technique of those who neatly provide the movies with their traditional Hollywood endings. For even the most mediocre of such stories ends on a note of satisfaction, with all the loose ends neatly tied together and the final assurance that everything is as it should be.

It is not that way in psychiatry. I have been called upon to examine individuals when every shred of sympathy and decency seemed to demand a negative finding: "There is nothing really wrong with this girl. All she needs is a little more sleep and a little fresh air, and she'll be better in a few weeks." And yet too often it doesn't work out that way. And the cold, unrelenting professional opinion—no matter how it is worded—must stab like a knife wound into the hearts of loved ones.

And then again I have examined frightened young men who had

depended upon a plea of insanity to spare them from a sentence of death . . . slightly wild-eyed, mentally abnormal youths spawned from the backwash of social neglect. And I have felt sorry for many of them. I have wished almost desperately that I could find some evidence to bolster their plea; for it is an awesome thing to sit in judgment while frightened eyes bore into yours with their pitiful plea for a chance to live. And yet too often the report must be negative, simply because their mental abnormality does not reach that arbitrary line which bounds the legal definition of insanity.

The psychiatrist must remind himself that his task is to appraise the mental and emotional status of the individual and not to consider the devious ways of ultimate justice. In compiling his report, he must paint the picture as he sees it for the God of Things as They Are.

Any reasonably normal person may be expected to have variable moods—up in the clouds on one occasion and down in the dumps on another. But normality is composed of moderation. The manic-depressive disposition goes to extremes. It rides the emotional roller-coaster not wisely but too well, plunging to unprecedented depths of depression and then flying to abnormal heights of ecstasy, with little attempted correlation with the immediate environment.

There are infinite variations of the manic-depressive psychoses and of the manic states, just as there are infinite variations of the state we speak of as normality. Sometimes the emotional roller-coaster gets stuck way up in the clouds, and sometimes it gets stalled at the bottom of the lowest dip.

The case of Virginia A. is a good illustration of the vagaries of this particular psychosis. Virginia was twenty-one years of age at the time of her first commitment. She was deeply depressed and spoke of suicide. She also professed an overwhelming fear of impending calamity, and the malady was diagnosed as a manic-depressive psychosis, depressed phase. (The emotional roller-coaster was stalled at the bottom of the lowest dip.) Investigation revealed that she had passed through a similar period of depression five years earlier and had recovered after several months without hospitalization or psychiatric attention of any kind. After several months in the hospital she showed all signs of recovery and was released.

But she was back again eleven years later with the same symptoms and the same diagnosis. She was deeply depressed, cried a great deal while in the hospital, and expressed the conviction that she would never recover, that she had made a mess of her life, and she'd be much better off dead. Again she recovered and again she was released.

But ten years later, and by now forty-three years of age, she was once more committed. But this time the symptoms were exactly opposite. She was happy, self-confident, and could see no reason why she should be in the hospital. (This time the emotional roller-coaster was stuck in the clouds.) She was talkative, overactive, and remarkably coöperative. But her conversation displayed an uncontrolled flight of ideas, together with delusions. By this time, fortunately, psychotherapy consisted of something more than confinement, catharsis, and the tepid bath. Virginia A. demonstrated quick and complete recovery after a brief course of electro-shock therapy and has remained well since.

Self-diagnosis in such cases is particularly difficult. And unfortunately, the impartial diagnosis of those intimately associated with us is likewise difficult. It is more or less a standard gag that the wrong member of the family is too often the first to visit the psychiatrist. Close daily association with an abnormal person may cause a sensitive soul to lose track of what is normal—just as a five-foot man married to a three-foot woman might get to thinking of himself as somewhat of a giant. Mr. Einstein could perhaps explain it.

A number of prominent psychologists have presented the conviction that a normal person can trace his fluctuating moods in definite cycles, as relentless as the tides. Good news, during an "up" period, will bring great happiness, while bad news will be absorbed without too great disturbance. "Oh well, those are the breaks of the game." But bad news during a "down" period will bring deep depression, discouragement and brooding; while good news is shunted aside as of no particular consequence: "So maybe I did win fifty bucks in a crap game. So what? That's only a drop in the bucket, compared to what I've lost over the years."

The theory is that our moods are not determined by events in the world around us, but that our moods determine how we appraise those events as they occur. Generally speaking, the person who is a slave to his moods, who tends to overindulge in matters of sex or of drink, who is lacking in moral control and who lacks casual and ordinary associations with a number and variety of friends—the person who is intolerant or rude or entirely unpredictable, would do well to consult a psychiatrist. It may be that he is still within the outer bounds of normality. But he could use the services of a trained surveyor to help locate the boundary. And he could use a little help in learning to live a more satisfying life.

One other broad type of psychoses should be considered—paranoia. Under this generalized banner are grouped a variety of paranoid states, and the lateral boundaries are not clearly defined, lapping over into the paranoid type of schizophrenia.

With startling consistency, acute feelings of inferiority may be found in the background of the paranoid individual, often associated with a sense of guilt with sexual origin. And the opening bid of paranoia is almost invariably introspection. Yes, self-study and self-analysis.

An intelligent and previously well-adjusted individual becomes extremely self-centered. This is known as the hypochondriacal stage, and it is undoubtedly at the very outset of this stage that the individual weighs himself, and finds himself wanting. He becomes unduly aware of his shortcomings and imagines, somehow, that others must be equally interested, and equally aware of these things. He lapses into the "Willie-pushed-me" technique—attempting to blame others, and subscribing to the theory that a good offense is the best defense.

At this stage he is suspicious, and tends to interpret the events of the entire world as applying to him, personally. He may complain of headaches or drowsiness, a lack of interest in his former hobbies, and an inability to concentrate. Casual remarks overheard are interpreted as concerning him; and generalized editorials about hoarders, speeders, drunken drivers, Communistic fellow travelers, or racial bigots, he considers to be direct reflections upon his good name, alone. It doesn't occur to him that these things might conceivably concern two other people.

Mrs. R., a married woman of middle age, first demonstrated psychotic tendencies following a severe infection which had kept her confined to her home for several months. She expressed the conviction that those around her were purposely keeping her in a state of poor health through a subtle program of poisoning.

At the time of her commitment she dramatically explained that the man posing as her husband was not the man she had married. She insisted that this man, who somewhat resembled her husband in appearance, had cunningly destroyed her true husband and had come to take his place; and that his purpose was to slowly destroy her, also. Nor did she believe that the two small boys living at her home were her real sons. They had been smuggled in by this impostor at some indefinite time, and were also involved in the plot to poison her.

There was, she admitted, no slight chance that she could be mistaken about this. The switch had been made so cunningly and so gradually that the impostors had fooled everybody else. But they couldn't fool her. When asked to explain how such a switch could be made "gradually," she became emotionally upset and incoherent, and insisted that the examiners were obviously included in the plot against her.

Mrs. R.'s family history revealed no cases of mental disorder, and her childhood had been considered entirely normal. She had been an excellent student in school and a prolific reader, although described as quiet, shy, and "dreamy." She had never been a good mixer, and had claimed no close personal friends.

Her delusions about her family continued, following her commitment, but reports from the hospital indicated that she was coöperative and able to adapt herself quite well in the new environment.

Many months elapsed before I again had a report about her case, but then I learned that Mrs. R. had changed from a model patient to a hospital hazard and a perplexing behavior problem. In the meantime, apparently, she had developed an entirely new delusion, and now believed herself to be a psychiatrist.

There may have been a certain amount of rationalization in this, as she insisted that her presence in the hospital was a matter of duty rather than confinement. She had previously studied psychology in school, and through reading and observation she had acquired an extensive vocabulary of psychiatric terms, most of which she used correctly.

But she was eternally creating a disturbance at the hospital in her contacts with other patients because of her determination to test their reflexes, whether they wished to coöperate or not. Most of the women patients with whom she came in contact had bruised kneecaps and thumb-worn pressure points. And she besieged them with eternal questions which she insisted were part of her psychoanalytic process.

After several years Mrs. R. showed such improvement that she was released to her family, with her early delusions about them apparently gone. But a later request for the records in her case indicated that she was again being committed in another state.

There is no sudden jump from the first stage of paranoia to the later stages. It is largely a matter of drifting. But gradually the patient resolves his earlier delusions into a more unified plot. Obviously, the entire world is highly organized in a heinous scheme against him. With this progression come hallucinations of the various senses. The delusions of persecution may bring association with some great martyr of history. Or, with a simple psychological back-flip, they bring delusions of grandeur. "If I weren't a very important personage, there wouldn't be so many people out to get me."

But unlike the schizophrenic, the paranoid individual may suffer no drastic mental deterioration. There comes no fog, and no vacuum. The victim may be able to carry on entirely normal conversations upon many different subjects, and the memory is not ordinarily impaired.

I once gave a pocket-worn partial pack of cigarettes to an elderly paranoid patient in the hospital who quite rationally and thoughtfully protested against taking my last cigarette. And only when I assured him that I had another pack in my topcoat downstairs did he accept the gift and express his thanks. It was a conversation such as might have taken place between any two normal individuals. A casual observer of that incident might have found it difficult to believe that one of us was abnormal—and even more difficult to guess which one.

And yet fifteen minutes later when I again came down the corridor, the same patient called me over to him and handed me a personal check made out for fifty thousand dollars.

"That's for the cigarettes," he explained humbly.

I thanked him, made a display of placing the check in my wallet, and turned to walk away. But once again he called me back and there was genuine concern in his eyes.

"Is that enough?" he asked anxiously. "I was going to make it out for a million dollars, but I'm trying to discipline myself." He laughed ruefully. "My financial secretary keeps getting after me for giving away too much money. He's a bore, but I try to humor him."

I assured the old gentleman that fifty thousand dollars seemed entirely adequate under the circumstances, and particularly so when one considered that the cigarette package had been half empty when I gave it to him.

"I'm glad," he said. "One thing I couldn't stand, would be for you to think I'd been a cheap skate."

And I imagine as the old boy puffed happily at each of his five-thousand-dollar cigarettes, he was able to feel infinitely superior to run-of-the-mill financiers who must content themselves with three-for-a-dollar cigars.

The ability of the paranoid individual to carry on perfectly lucid conversations upon a variety of subjects is often confusing to the uninformed observer who, for some reason, is inclined to view sanity as an all-or-nothing proposition.

One of the principal characteristics of true paranoia is the steadfast nature of the delusion. The patient is not Napoleon today and Julius Caesar tomorrow. Multiple, changeable, and unsystematized delusions characterize the paranoid states which lap over toward the field of other psychoses and constitute the Miscellaneous section of the catalogue.

William K., fifty-four years old at the time of his admission to the hospital, represented a reasonably typical case of true paranoia. There was no record of mental illness elsewhere in the family, but Mr. K. presented a long history of mental illness and legal entanglements, and he had been previously hospitalized in a number of different states. He had completed two years of college before dropping out of school and entering the retail hardware and appliance business. In this he had been modestly successful for several years, but then failed completely. He had been forced into involuntary bankruptcy, losing not only his business but his personal automobile and practically everything except the clothes upon his back.

Shortly after this he became obsessed with the idea that he had been defrauded by a conspiracy involving not only his former creditors, but also the circuit judge and the county authorities as well. Because of the delusional nature of his charges, he was committed to the state hospital in the state where he then resided.

His life was then devoted to his attempts to secure what he believed to be justice. It is interesting to note that he subscribed to and successfully completed correspondence courses in law—courses requiring considerable study and concentration—and actually completed some of these studies while an inmate of a mental institution.

After this, he commenced to draw up lengthy complaints in legal form. He was committed in two other states, and promptly added new names to his list of persecutors, convinced that the psychiatric examiners, hospital attendants, and even some of the other patients were involved in the original conspiracy against him.

After his final commitment, Mr. K. refused to take part in ward activities, but spent his time in his room, writing out lengthy presentations of his case. After several years his psychosis was modified by the changes incident to advancing age, but in general he retained the original delusions until he died at sixty-five of a tumor of the adrenal gland.

These psychoses—all of them—stand as the end-result of the individual's inward adjustment to his environment when he has been unable to make the customary outward adjustment. The corporate cells of the human body struggle to remain solvent, to continue in business, and to retain a certain amount of self-respect, even if they have to pad the books, falsify the records, and present a purely fictitious report at the regular stockholders' meeting.

There is perhaps only one thing more fabulous than the intricate mechanism of the subconscious mind, and that's the ingenuity of the men who have attempted to explain it.

# 14

*Sometimes we may learn more from a man's errors,
than from his virtues.*—LONGFELLOW

AT THE TIME of my early studies in Vienna, just before the turn of
the century, Sigmund Freud was an outstanding neurologist and had
gained an international reputation as an exponent of psychoanalysis.
He had not, however, become a legend. And his name was little
known to the man in the street. At the time, he was struggling with
his manuscript of *The Interpretation of Dreams,* due to be published
in 1900 and destined to make him one of the most controversial figures
of the era.

To me, he was but one of many distinguished men under whom
I studied. And, frankly, one of the less impressive. I had no way of
knowing that the passing years would endow him with a great controversial significance. And I was as unimpressed in the presence of
greatness as were the dock-hands of ancient Genoa, picking their way
around the dreamy-eyed offspring of Domenico Colombo.

Most of Freud's demonstrations which I attended were performed
with young women. In the presence of the class, he would ask the
most intimate questions about their sexual experiences, or he would
triumphantly explain some deeply hidden sexual significance in their
most casual thoughts and statements and dream sequences. And I am
afraid Dr. Freud impressed me as a rather pedantic man with a one-
track mind.

I am sorry to say that I learned a great deal more about Sigmund
Freud by reading about him than I ever learned by listening to him.

And I had to wait until he was heralded by the world at large before I could find any deep personal appreciation for his great pioneering work, and before I could derive any satisfaction from explaining that I used to know him when.

For one thing, my early days in Vienna were dismally darkened by a covering cloud of homesickness. It was my first trip abroad and I had a tendency to compare things with the way we'd done them back home. And practically everything in Vienna suffered from the contrast.

I was handicapped by my inexperience in the use of foreign languages. The patients with whom we worked had come from all parts of Europe, and they spoke in many different tongues. Dr. Freud would assign us to an interview with some particular patient and then painstakingly compare our findings with his own. And in our very first attempt at such collaboration, I spent more than an hour with a slightly psychopathic woman attempting to interview her with my limited command of the German language until finally she asked in apparent disgust, "Herr Doktor, can you speaken not English?" And I spent the rest of my time with her wondering just who should be studying the mental status of whom?

It is a matter of record that Christopher Columbus was not the first man to believe that the world was round. He was merely the first man willing to risk his neck in an effort to prove it; and willing to dedicate his life to the project despite sneers of derision.

It is equally true that Sigmund Freud was not the first man to envision the potential values of psychoanalysis in exploring the unconscious. (He preferred to call it the unconscious rather than the subconscious.) Nor was he the first man to use psychoanalysis as a tool. He was merely the first man willing to risk his reputation and to dedicate his life to that bit of psychic navigation. He is popularly known as the father of psychoanalysis. And it doesn't pay to get too technical, in determining the legitimacy of the offspring.

The passing years proved that Columbus was in error when he thought he had reached the East Indies. It was faulty judgment when he looked at the red-skinned natives and called them Indians. He had made a great discovery, but he interpreted it incorrectly.

There is some reason to suppose that Sigmund Freud was guilty of equally erroneous interpretations when he went exploring into the uncharted seas of the unconscious. But a reasonable margin for error should be a standard allowance for those who sail beyond previous horizons.

Dr. Joseph Breuer, with whom Freud was associated as a young man, is credited with the original premise upon which Freud built his life's work: the conjecture that certain physical symptoms of neurotic patients possibly spring from peculiar mental or emotional drives, affected by the patient's past experience.

Fascinated by this premise, young Freud took off for Paris to further his study under Jean Martin Charcot. And it was from the lips of Janet, one of Charcot's associates, that Freud heard reference to the "subconscious." But Janet hastened to explain that he used the term merely as a convenient "figure of speech." He believed that certain alien disturbances upset the personality during hysteria, and "subconscious" seemed about as good a term as any. Or, *idées inconscientes.*

Freud, however, remained tantalized by the possibilities. Perhaps the figure of speech was more apt than even Janet realized. Here could be the key to the puzzle first propounded by Breuer. And he embarked upon a program of counterespionage in the field of psychic conflict, attempting to smoke out the mental "French underground" in Charcot's clinic.

Freud, like Columbus, knew in advance what he hoped to prove. And the emphasis upon sex was hardly the result of reading too many of the wrong kind of magazines while awaiting his turn in a barbershop.

The starting point of Freudian thought is the same jumping-off-place where all philosophies begin: There must be some plausible reason for man's existence on this earth. Surely there must be some long-range reason why the human animal exists, and there must be some greater responsibility than merely keeping up the payments on the mortgage.

It is not a far-fetched conclusion that persons living today have one overwhelming responsibility: to connect the future to the past, and

somehow to preserve the precious spark of life that started with creation and is supposed to endure at least until Armageddon. From here
it is a small step to the next conclusion: Our real purpose on this
earth is to reproduce our kind. And the reproduction process being
what it is, you are automatically up to your ears in the subject of sex.
Everything else becomes an irrelevant by-product.

Reducing a complex host of theories beyond the point of excusable
simplicity, one may commence to glimpse the approach to Freudian
thought by envisioning people on this earth with but one basic reason
for existence, and endowed with one primary instinct: Man was given
space on the earth for the same reason that a farmer provides space
in his barnyard for a brood sow. It's not that she's such charming
company, nor that she adds materially to the beauty of the landscape.
It's merely that she's an expert in the fine art of reproduction.

Even the most bitter critics of Sigmund Freud concede that he
rendered a great service to humanity: He removed the subject of sex
from the conversational back closet and introduced it into the parlor.
But it is important to realize that he gave the subject a much broader
interpretation than will ever be found intimated in a burlesque theatre. Caresses, love pats, holding hands, masculine chest-puffing and
feminine coquetry, parental pride and youthful adoration—in fact the
entire structure of love-inspired behavior, he grouped under the heading of "Sex." He envisoned sex as the reason behind many acts of
human behavior, and not as the ultimate aim of such acts. And there
is a subtle but significant difference.

Those who seek to find the reason behind any phenomenon must
presuppose that a reason exists. And Freud, in general, beheld the
unconscious as the seat of deep dark emotions inherited, somehow,
from the recesses of the past, and similar to those which control the
behavior of all life.

There is something in the nature of the black widow spider, for
instance, that causes her to destroy her mate. There is no reason to
question her motives, nor is there reason to suspect that it weighs
heavily upon her conscience. She does the old boy in, simply because

that's the way she is. It's an instinct of the species, and probably there's nothing personal in it, so far as she is concerned.

And similarly, in his controversial theories wrapped round with sexual significance, Freud spoke of latent instincts buried deep in the unconscious. Nor can his theories be understood nor honestly appraised by those who overlook this significant factor. Hidden desires of the unconscious may never break through to the status of conscious thought or action. They are held in confinement by ethics, training, tradition, fear, respect, and a gradual refinement of the species.

Suppose, through countless generations, you could teach the black widow spider to be more tolerant of her mate—give her a code of ethics and a book of etiquette and make her a highly compassionate type of critter. Still, deep down inside (or as deep down as it's possible to get, inside a spider) there would remain that ancient instinct which could not be banished with training, any more than a vermiform appendix could be done away with through diet.

Likewise, back in the era before Emily Post, graduated income taxes, allowance for dependents, and the theory that two can live as cheaply as one, there had to be certain inborn motives in the human species to regulate behavior and to insure the development of those attitudes that would be beneficial to the species in the long run. And these hidden drives and unrecognized forces perhaps continue to wield their influence upon us, regardless of where we choose to draw the line that is supposed to separate rational from irrational behavior.

Conflict is the inevitable result when our inner drives suggest we should do one thing, while our training and our acquired social graces insist that we should do something else. Even a tired old farm horse can develop the nervous jitters if the reins pull "gee" while the driver shouts "haw." And in this deep conflict between inner drives and acquired inhibitions, Freud beheld a possible explanation for peculiar neurotic behavior. But in pursuing his theories beyond the previous horizons he had a tendency to lead faster than many of us could follow.

If I was unimpressed by Dr. Freud and his rather fabulous theories during those early days in Vienna, I shudder to think what his reactions must have been toward some of his younger American students.

And there were many of us. Even then, the lust for American dollars was something magnificent to behold, and we generally shared the best that Vienna had to offer.

Nor do I recall that many of us were particularly endowed with intellectual modesty. We shopped with finicky appetites among the profound thoughts of the world's greatest psychiatric explorers. And then in the evenings we'd gather in our various rooms and sip beer, and trade impressions and pass judgment upon all that we had seen and heard. And sometimes, too, we'd add thoughts and ideas of our own, and attempt to decide during lengthy discourse just which theories we'd care to accept and which could be quietly discarded.

There seemed nothing particularly incongruous in this at the time. Most of us were comparatively young. All of us had taken our medical degrees back home and some of us had established a certain amount of practice. None doubted his ability to make contributions to the growing store of knowledge. And each, of course, felt peculiarly endowed with an unusual amount of common sense which would enable him, by sheer logic, to separate the wheat from the chaff, the fact from the fiction, the basic truths from the far-fetched misconceptions.

Oddly enough, I believe these nocturnal bull sessions contributed substantially to our progress of understanding, for they brought forth many arguments and many illustrations that never could have been accommodated in a more academic atmosphere. And the leisurely logic of a beer-drinking companion somehow seemed more convincing than the arbitrary and often pedantic statements of the great men under whom we studied and with whom time was such a precious commodity.

Sigmund Freud, I imagine, would have been more than a little aghast if he could have placed an ear to the keyhole and heard his formal and often formidable theories, such as that of the Oedipus complex, broken down into trivial chunks, and then devoured like pretzels at a beer bust.

King Oedipus, in case the legend slips your mind, was predestined to kill his father and marry his mother. Forewarned by a soothsayer of this revolting development, the father had attempted to do away with his son. But as so often happens in stories of this type, the son was found by shepherds and raised to manhood. During the course of the plot he managed to kill his father and marry his mother, unaware of his true relationship to either of them. And then in the best tradition of the old Greek tragedies, Oedipus became aware of his folly, blinded himself, and begged for banishment at the final curtain.

Despite the great influence of this drama upon Greek and European literature during the classical period, it perhaps would have been almost as well in the long run if the shepherds had failed to find young Oedipus; if he'd died as a baby and the theatre customers had all gone home early on that particular evening. For it is the Oedipus complex that gives rise to some of the most controversial doctrines of Sigmund Freud.

Roughly stated, the Oedipus complex finds in the son a deep unconscious desire toward the mother. And since, under the Freudian banner, there can be no such thing as Platonic friendship in the primitive cauldron of the unconscious, you are permitted to think what you will about the nature of those desires. Running parallel to it is the son's unconscious desire to kill his father. This is the competitive angle of the eternal triangle, and it is matched in the opposite gender by the Electra complex, wherein the daughter desires the father, and has unconscious desires to dispose of the mother who is her competitor for Papa's affections.

And even though more than half a century has elapsed, I can remember with remarkable clarity the night when young Dr. Joe dramatically blew his top, announced that he was through with the study of psychiatry in general and Dr. Freud in particular, and that he was heading for home as quickly as he could pack his things and arrange for transportation.

"I've spent good money to listen to a lot of damn foolish tripe," he announced bitterly. "I've gagged on some of the stuff you men seem to swallow, and I've tried to tell myself that you're all intelligent men and that if you can swallow it I should force myself to do the same. But, by God, if you can sit here and let somebody tell you that you had sexual desires for your own mother and a secret yearning to kill your own father, when you were still in diapers, then you don't even need to see me off on the train. I want to forget I ever knew men like you!"

The explosion was so sudden and so bitter that most of us sat back aghast. Someone laughed nervously and tried to ease the tension. "Aw, come on, Joe. Sit down and have a beer, and let's talk this thing over just as we always have in the past."

But Dr. Joe was in no mood to be placated. The lines of his mouth were drawn tight, and the fire in his soul seemed to reflect through his eyes. And I can remember that I felt soft and morally flabby, and a little too wishy-washy. For he had expressed in dramatic fashion the same reactions that I had purposely pushed aside for reasons of convenience and perhaps emotional laziness.

There followed a long and embarrassing silence. And then it was the tall and cadaverous and usually silent Dr. Brockheim who broke the stillness. His voice, with just the slightest hint of accent, was calm but biting:

"I should have no intention of seeing you off on the train. I have not as yet made up my mind about Dr. Freud's Oedipus complex, but already I can see where it serves a worthy purpose. It separates those who think, from those who merely feel."

The tension in the room was ominous. Young Dr. Joe took one step toward Dr. Brockheim, who was smiling calmly and winding his long fingers around a beer stein. And then, somehow, all of the flame died out of Dr. Joe; cut short, no doubt, by the unexpected backfire.

"Well, if that's the sort of thing you have to think about in order to be a thinker, you can count me out," he announced weakly. And then Dr. Brockheim took the floor, almost uncontested.

"Always in the world there will be men who will say, 'This cannot be true, because I do not wish to believe it.' Or, 'This does not make sense, because I do not understand it.' Always there will be men who will say, 'I will believe in things that are invisible, only when I can see them; and I will believe in the existence of an unconscious, only when I become conscious of it.'"

"That's what's so damned ridiculous about it," Dr. Joe snorted. "He stands up there and spouts these asinine theories of his, and he tries to prove what he says today by quoting what he said yesterday. He hasn't a damned shred of real evidence to back up any of it."

Dr. Brockheim smiled crookedly. "I seem to recall that Dr. Joe is somewhat of an expert at watching how the dice behave, at a certain establishment, and deciding whether they are loaded. Dr. Freud prefers to study how people behave, and I am sure his theories are as reliable as are Dr. Joe's."

Young Dr. Joe winced slightly for he'd been touched in a tender spot. "That isn't any theory of mine. Those dice are loaded and, by God, if I could get hold of them and cut them open I could prove it to you. I'll bet you five hundred dollars!"

But Dr. Brockheim brushed the rebuttal aside with a wave of his hand. "The point is, you haven't proved it as yet, and so far your argument is just a theory. You reason to yourself, 'If the dice were loaded, that would explain why they behave in this peculiar fashion.' But you don't have any more real evidence than Dr. Freud does. I doubt if you have as much."

Dr. Joe, by now, had sunk to the arm of a chair and another gabfest had been definitely launched for the evening.

"I will tell you how I feel about it," Dr. Brockheim continued. "When I was just a little boy, I had a theory. I believed in Santa Claus. My theory explained many things, to my complete satisfaction. It explained why there were toys under the tree on Christmas morning. It explained what had become of the piece of cake I had left on the mantel. It explained why I had heard bells jingling in the middle of the night, and why there were large footprints of ashes and soot leading from the fireplace to the Christmas tree.

"Then when I became older I commenced to wonder about my theory. I went with my father to the roof to help put on new shakes, and I noticed that the hole in the chimney was small. I asked myself: How could a man who leaves such big footprints get down such a small opening? I learned, then, that my early theory had been wrong, even though it had seemed to explain everything at the time."

"And that's exactly what's going to happen to a lot of these damn fool theories we're wasting our time on today," Dr. Joe cut in triumphantly. But Dr. Brockheim merely nodded his head.

"There can be little doubt of it. But we must learn to creep before we learn to walk. Either a man must be willing to believe something, or he must be content with believing nothing. I have never felt it was a waste of time to believe in Santa Claus. My theory was all wrong, but it taught me to see the beauty of Christmas and to feel the excitement of the Yuletide, and it taught me to love Christmas carols, and it answered all my questions at the time."

And the years have proved that Dr. Brockheim was unusually astute. Many of the controversial theories Sigmund Freud first offered to a skeptical world have come in for extensive revision if not outright cancellation. And yet much of the progress of the past half century has grown directly from his pioneering work.

In his early association with Breuer, Sigmund Freud had observed the use of *abreaction,* or the tell-Papa-everything-and-get-it-off-your-chest type of psychotherapy, which was to provide the framework for his later methods of analysis. But it was far from new, even then. Types of religious confession could be traced back to antiquity and the getting-it-off-the-chest routine saw its start, no doubt, shortly after the dawn of human language.

However, like Mama using a nut-pick to adjust the set-screws on the television set, Sigmund Freud used an old tool for a new purpose. He felt that the hidden drives of the unconscious might reveal clues to their nature, particularly if the individual could train himself to speak first, and think afterward. His techniques of free association were intended to reveal orally those spontaneous thoughts which the adult has learned to disregard in usual conversation. The patient in psychoanalysis must learn to leap before he looks, and give voice to his thoughts before appraising them. And to this extent, Freud went beyond the previous boundaries of the happy little philosophy that confession is good for the soul.

To explain his theories, Sigmund Freud was called upon to introduce an entire, new terminology, just as the geographical explorer finds it his honored duty to give names to all the newly discovered rivers and bays and mountain peaks.

He envisioned the human psyche, like all Gaul, as divided into three parts; and these he designated as the id, the ego, and the super-ego. Unconscious drives are buried in the id. The ego is the surveyor of the here and now. And the super-ego, in effect, is the conscience fortified by acquired morality and inhibitions. Sexual drives, for example, originate in the id. The ego looks over the landscape, beholds an opportunity for the drives to find release, and weighs the chances of getting away with it. But the super-ego may exercise its power of veto when it finds the scheme a matter of questionable ethics. And thus the upstairs maid goes quietly on about her business, possibly unaware of the momentary glint in the master's eye.

But it doesn't end there. The id is a primitive place concerned with basic desires. It has no conscience and it doesn't listen to reason. You could compare it to the wild-eyed youngster who lives in a third-floor flat, screaming at the top of his lungs that he wants a pony. Mama and Papa may explain with unusual patience that it's impossible to keep a pony in an apartment, that the landlord wouldn't permit it, that the family budget couldn't accommodate such an expenditure, and that a pony would be most unhappy, stabled in a pullman bath. And the youngster, after listening soberly to all this, offers one rebuttal louder than ever: "But I want a pony!" The id, with its basic drives, is no more inclined to listen to reason.

Because they can't stand the eternal screaming of their offspring, and because they've read a book on psychology, Mama and Papa may attempt a program of substitution: "Let's have a good talk with the landlord and see if he won't let us keep a puppy in our apartment. Then maybe Junior will get so interested in the puppy, he'll forget about wanting the pony."

Freud envisioned a similar drama in the human psyche, as the ego strives to find some substitute-outlet for the desires of the id, which would at the same time be acceptable to the super-ego. Only Freud called it sublimation rather than substitution, and his is perhaps the better term.

An infant, for example, derives a certain unconscious sexual satisfaction from the act of urinating. If the pleasure is extreme, he may be difficult to train. But through sublimation those basic drives may find an outlet in some more worthy social activity and you'll possibly find him, years later, as an enthusiastic member of the volunteer fire department.

Under the Freudian theory, sadistic drives within the id may be sublimated so that the individual becomes a surgeon, or a meat-cutter. And the scientist peering eagerly through his microscope may be finding a sublimated outlet for a Peeping Tom complex, inspired by a youthful curiosity about sex which induced him at an early age to secretly borrow Papa's binoculars and stare at the upstairs windows across the street.

As many had done before him, Freud observed a somewhat standardized pattern of interest in the growing child. The infant is preoccupied with his own needs and appetites. The small schoolboy seeks the companionship of other small schoolboys. And the adolescent turns his interest to members of the opposite sex. Freud differed from those before him by insisting that sexual drives commenced not at puberty but at birth. He differed, also, by suggesting that neuroses would be impossible in a person with a normal sex life.

Thus, the pervert and self-exhibitionist has never successively outgrown the "self-interest" drives of the infant. And the homosexual has never sublimated the latency, or small-schoolboy period of development. The deep-throated female with the boyish haircut and a mania for wearing men's shirts has never completely recovered from her I-was-robbed attitude—first born in that instant when she realized that her little brother had a penis and she had none.

Obviously, there can be no peace in the upstairs flat where Junior is screaming his head off because he wants a pony; where the unrelenting landlord will make no compromise to allow the boy to have a puppy; and where a distraught father paces the floor and periodically blows his top: "I'm going to go nuts, if that kid doesn't stop scream-ing!"

And according to Freud, there can be no peace in the human psyche, when the unrelenting sexual drives of the id find no release, when the super-ego remains unrelenting, and when the ego is caught in the middle, between "I want to" and "You mustn't."

I could not in honesty say that I ever accepted Dr. Freud's involved and sex-related theories any more readily than did Dr. Joe. Each demonstration and each explanation I accepted with a grain of salt, and I soon shied away from such a saline diet. Through the years that have followed, I have never considered myself a disciple of the Freudian school. And more particularly in recent years I have inclined toward the belief that sex, like bathtub gin during the prohibition era, has been magnified far out of proportion to its real significance. (This is perhaps a viewpoint made possible only by my advancing age.)

Life is possible without sex. The amoeba, for example, has endured for thousands of years without it. The division into sexes appears in the higher types of organisms, and it is reasonable to suppose that it serves some broader purpose than to promote the sale of double plumbing in service stations. In the final analysis, it serves about the same purpose as does the gunnysack in a three-legged race. It is the common bond that keeps the species together. It is the mixing machine that unifies hereditary traits. It is the blotter that slowly sops up individual and racial differences, weeds out the ugly and the mal-formed, and makes it possible, generally, for people to look like people.

Only in the human species have we distorted it out of proportion to other normal functions, and only in the Western half of the world have we used it as a sort of universal flavoring to spice everything from literature to display advertising.

Sometimes I'm inclined to wonder if Sigmund Freud actually per-formed such a commendable service to mankind, in removing the subject of sex from the conversational back closet and introducing it into the parlor, and particularly if it is going to throw the room so completely out of balance.

And yet despite any personal reservations that have prevented me

from becoming a rah-rah boy of the Freudian school, I am quite sure
that the contributions of Sigmund Freud toward the advancement of
psychotherapy far outweigh the contributions of any other ten men
I have met in more than half a century of psychiatric study and practice. And oddly enough, the best illustration I ever chanced to come
across, demonstrating unconscious motivation as envisioned by Sigmund Freud, was a little incident that took place a number of years
ago on Olvera Street in Los Angeles, explained by a man who probably had never heard of psychiatry.

I had paused at a little stand to examine some curios when a bright-
eyed old Mexican gentleman thrust a small brown object into my hand
and instructed: "You hold heem. Pretty soon he jomp."

When I drew back the old gentleman hastened to reassure me. "He
no hurt you. He's broncho bean. You hold heem, he jump."

I examined the thing curiously in the palm of my hand—a parched-
looking little bean that appeared perfectly harmless. But even as I
watched, the thing somehow miraculously flipped over.

"What did you call it?" I asked.

"He's broncho bean, five cents," the old man explained. "Sometimes you call heem jomping bean."

It was my first experience with such a phenomenon and I was
curious. The old gentleman, however, seemed a little reluctant to
answer my questions, no doubt feeling that a five-cent purchase price
shouldn't include the revelation of trade secrets. But when I persisted
he finally gave in.

"I tell you. Inside, he's a little worm. You hold heem in your hand,
he get warm. Then he feel good and jomp, like thees. So when he
jomp, he make the bean jomp. Savvy?"

I savvied. And I think from that five-cent investment in a Mexican
jumping bean I gained my best and most dramatic illustration of the
more highly involved Freudian theories about unconscious motivations.

Like the little larva of a moth inside the bean, our unconscious
motivations are not apparent from the surface. But under certain
influences they jomp. And when they jomp, they make us jomp.
Savvy?

Both Freud and the aged Mexican gentleman may have been mistaken so far as incidental details are concerned, about the true nature of the "worm" on the inside. But apparently both had the basic theory pretty well in mind.

# 15

*Sit in reverie, and watch the changing color of the waves
that break upon the idle seashore of the mind.*

—LONGFELLOW

MEN, FROM TIME immemorial, have been tantalized by the dream of
reading other men's minds, of scanning their innermost thoughts. And
such dreams have not been entirely empty. Even the family dog may
learn to interpret the mood of his master, by noting reaction habits,
the posture, the tone of the voice, and so on. And certainly the mood
is indicative of the general nature of the thoughts.

And yet when Sigmund Freud went exploring into the depths of the
unconscious, he introduced the need for a new type of telepathic bi-
focals. The problem we faced during those early days in Vienna was
not merely to read the thoughts in a patient's conscious mind, but to
peer beyond and behold the subconscious thoughts and attitudes and
impressions of which the patient was not even aware.

To meet this seemingly impossible assignment, Freud experimented
with and extended the use of psychoanalysis and standardized its techniques by training those of us who studied with him. He continued
daily to compile data, wrote prolifically, turned the spotlight of analysis
upon himself and upon others close around him, prowled through
voluminous research and, in short, dedicated his sleeping as well as
his waking hours to the project. For even his dreams went into the
melting pot and contributed their share to the growing volume of data.

For a great many years we struggled with our basic techniques inside
a vacuum of almost complete oblivion. The public looked upon us

with neither interest nor disdain, but generally looked upon us not at all. Hundreds of men who had learned the basic tenets of psychoanalysis under Freud struck out upon their own, striving to alter, improve, or perfect this unique but rather unwieldy tool of psychiatric examination. The mortality rate among psychoanalytic theories was appalling.

After my return from Europe and my subsequent marriage—and more particularly after the honeymoon was over—I insisted that my wife relate her dreams to me each morning, immediately upon awakening. And breakfast at our house developed into something like a series of light snacks grabbed hurriedly by a pair of deep-sea divers bobbing erratically up and down out of the unconscious.

This sort of thing went on for nearly a year, until the morning of the mutiny over the coffee cups when my wife announced that she was through with the experiment. "You spend so much time exploring my subconscious mind," she protested, "that my conscious mind is dying of loneliness. Why can't we just sit down some morning and talk about the weather, and behave like normal people for a change?"

She felt so strongly about it that, when our first child was born, she delivered an ultimatum from the hospital bed: "I've talked to the doctor, Jim. He tells me we have a baby girl, and not a guinea pig. I want you to promise me that you'll treat her like a daughter, and not like a laboratory specimen."

Similar scenes of conscious and unconscious conflict, I imagine, were taking place within other homes where psychiatrists and would-be psychoanalysts were struggling to learn more about unconscious exploration. But the world at large paid little heed.

Particularly from about 1910 through the early 1930's, there commenced to appear new schools of psychoanalysis, breaking away from the Freudian concept and placing less stress upon the subject of sex. The process was not unlike that of cleaning up the robust smoking room story for presentation on the radio.

But social acceptance wasn't the sole inspiration. The founders of the new schools had been unable to see eye-to-eye with Freud . . . and they were now unable to see eye-to-eye with each other.

A more cynical person might compare them to men fishing through the hole in the ice, chopped by Sigmund Freud. And although they all used the same kind of bait and the same kind of tackle and roughly the same technique, still, no two could agree on what kind of fish were down there. And none could prove the others wrong because none, as yet, had landed a blessed thing.

All schools of psychoanalysis agree that there are strange forces swimming around deep in the unconscious, but they haven't agreed on the nature of those forces.

Freud, as we've noted, envisioned the unconscious as the center of powerful inherited instincts that have come down through the centuries with the species; latent forces lurking beneath the surface, which served mankind through an earlier era and which, like the vermiform appendix, have not entirely disappeared . . . and which are capable of acting up and causing misery to the man of today.

Adler envisioned the unconscious more as a storage place—a convenient little suitcase where the individual can hide away the thoughts and incidents he doesn't choose to remember consciously. The child starts his journey through life with the suitcase practically empty, except for a few recognized instincts he's certain to need on the way. But as he journeys along he fills the case with the products of his own experience. And trouble develops when he tries to file away too many feelings of inferiority or embarrassment. The overcrowded bag may spring its lock and spill out onto the sidewalk its assortment of dirty laundry, revealing to the eyes of the world the very things the individual has tried to conceal.

Jung envisioned the unconscious more as a prefabricated conscience or soul . . . a God-given pattern of "the good life" . . . a radio beam to guide the individual through the fog and confusion of a complex world toward a proper destination. When the individual strays too far from the kind of life Destiny has chosen for him, then the radio beam grows faint and life loses its direction and its purpose. The course of the individual becomes erratic, and his unpredictable actions constitute a hazard to himself and to others.

Rank, bless his far-sighted soul, took issue with the theory that analysis should be aimed at driving the neurotics back into the human herd and that rugged individualism should be discouraged. He beheld in the neurotic individual a strong similarity to the creative individual —if, in fact, the two did not actually overlap. And he contended that psychotherapy should consist of providing the neurotic individual with creative outlets in the fields of art, religion, philosophy, and so on.

Each school of psychoanalysis has its loyal followers and each has its bitter critics. And then there are those who, in a spirit of compromise, have taken a little from each school and developed their own hybrid type of theory. And the most amazing thing of it all is this: Each, in his own way, has had his successes and his failures.

During my early years of medical practice in Los Angeles I made an honest effort to keep abreast of the various evolving theories; to weigh the arguments and to appraise the evidence. My days were filled with routine medical chores, but my evenings were given over to reading, study, and contemplation. I was a transient student of the various schools. And when time permitted, I dashed frantically across the continent and across the Atlantic Ocean to listen to the spreading debate. I have in my day, I believe, met nearly every psychiatrist of note, and heard his personal endorsements of his own particular theories. I have faced the inevitable concession that these great men are far better informed than I ever will be, and I have recognized the irony of my own situation, attempting to choose among their theories.

During these days, leading up to the early 1930's, there was considerable interdenominational rivalry among the various schools—the entrenched belief that if one was right, the rest must necessarily be wrong. And the debate at times grew bitter. And then, subtly, there commenced to emerge a you-go-to-your-church-and-I'll-go-to-mine type of analytical tolerance . . . a realization that the points of difference were not so significant as the points of similarity. At approximately the same time, the Baptists were admitting that possibly the Methodists weren't all consigned to perdition. And the owner of a Chevrolet was reluctantly conceding to the owner of a Ford, "Well, that's a good car, too." It was the dawn of an era of remarkable tolerance, reaching even into the isolated world of psychoanalytical theory.

And then at about this time someone in Hollywood, looking for new worlds to exploit, chanced to come upon the story of psychiatry. There erupted an epidemic of "psychological" movies. Psychiatrists with thick, guttural accents and treacherous souls stormed menacingly through the soap operas and the printed fields of fiction.

Having exhausted all possible gags about California weather, radio comedians turned their attention with understandable zeal to the psychoanalytical couch. It provided all the elements for a gag-writer's field day, with a subtle and implied combination of science and seduction.

And we who had struggled so long in the dark found ourselves blinded by the powerful beams of artificial light, while our magnified shadows must have been awesome to behold.

And from it all, I'm afraid the average person has gained a rather weird conception of what takes place during psychoanalysis.

Actually, the couch is nonessential. During my early days in Vienna I never even heard of such a device. Freud, at the time, was developing his technique of free association, during which the patient is urged to express all thoughts that come to his mind, without reservation or censorship. But a reasonably comfortable chair was considered a perfectly appropriate setting for the patient.

The use of the couch is psychological. Its purpose has been recognized through experience, and is easily understandable if one envisions the nature and the idea of it without allowing the imagination to go skipping off at a tangent.

It is not easy for a normal person to give voice to all thoughts as they occur to him, and invariably the technique must be acquired. A host of inhibitions must be overcome, for all of us have learned to weigh our thoughts and to discard those that seem unworthy of oral expression.

As children, when we were inclined to babble on without self-imposed censorship, we were told that children should be seen and not heard. When we started off to school, we were warned that certain family secrets should not be related to the teacher. In adolescence we were drilled on the importance of not babbling intimate information to strangers. And in adult life, we have been reminded again and again that incessant talking is the keynote of the bore. "Blessed is the man who, having nothing to say, abstains from giving in words evidence of the fact." In addition, all of us have at some time been greeted with jeers of derision when we've given voice to sudden thoughts without pausing to consider how ridiculous they might sound; and the subconscious mind is on guard to prevent a repetition of this embarrassing circumstance.

It is not easy, then, to sit down across the desk from an analyst, look him squarely in the eye, and give forth with a continuous flow of talk and trivia without self-imposed censorship. And from the analyst's standpoint, it is not easy to sit and look impassively interested in all that flows forth without giving visible signs of boredom or impatience, or without stifling a yawn.

Experience has demonstrated that it is far better for the patient to rest comfortably on the couch, with the analyst out of his range of vision. For once he has overcome his inhibitions and got the hang of it, the patient will at times almost forget that the analyst is present in the room. He is not talking to the analyst, in the usual sense of ordinary conversation. He is, rather, thinking aloud. He is like the fictional character of a radio drama who's been left alone in a room, and who must express his thoughts out loud to prevent that radio catastrophe of a stony silence.

The ease of expressing random thoughts increases with practice. In the first session, the patient is naturally self-conscious. His first attempts are apt to be formal and hesitant, and his voice unsure:

"Well, I was born in 1903. I've been married twenty-six years in June. I have three children, Pat and Mike and Helen. Pat is the oldest. I'm an insurance claim adjuster. I like to play golf—and—well —that's about all I can think of, right now." And there will follow a prolonged stretch of silence if the analyst does not ease the tension with casual questions.

The process is like attempting to write a letter to someone to whom you haven't written in years. You may sit for a long time chewing nervously at the top of the pen or staring blankly out the window, honestly convinced that there's nothing to say—nothing that's really worth mentioning. But if the correspondence should continue—if you should keep on writing letters every day to that person—you would soon find that topics to fill a half-dozen pages would flow readily from your pen.

It is like that with successive visits to the analyst: difficult at first to find things to talk about; almost impossible, later on, to find time to express all the things that come to your mind.

The analyst, during all this, is neither aloof nor forward. He does not lead the conversation. Ordinarily he does not interrupt to ask questions. But neither does he play the sphinx, nor pretend to be the little man who isn't there.

He wants the patient to be almost oblivious of the fact that he's in the room. But not entirely oblivious. The patient is deeply engrossed in attempting to pull up thoughts and memories and impressions from his subconscious mind and to express them orally. And the analyst, like the professional and highly efficient guide on a fishing trip, is right there to lend a hand if needed—to offer expert advice on the technique, and to reach out with a conversational gaff-hook to help bring an elusive idea to the surface.

Actually, of course, the analyst is observing the patient at all times. He is possibly less interested in what is said, than in why it is said, and how it is said.

Many silly notions have been publicly tossed about, concerning just what the analyst watches for amid the stream of free-association conversation. And writers, for obvious reasons, choose to dramatize the more unusual incidents that develop—just as illustrators choose to portray the placer miner picking up a gold nugget from the sluice box, rather than portraying him shoveling the hundreds of tons of muck that must be handled in the process. The ratio between muck and nuggets is as lop-sided in the analyzing business as in the placer-mining business.

What's more, I once met a placer miner in the fabulous Mother Lode country who told me he'd been working his claim for years without finding a nugget large enough to pick up with his bare fingers. But he made it pay through the accumulation of "colors," hardly larger than flyspecks, that gathered in the bottom of his sluice box. No single speck of gold, in itself, had ever been of great value or worthy of a half-hearted cheer. But all of them, together, he told me, had been sufficient to renew the grubstake. And there was always the chance that tomorrow might be better.

And in the typical analysis, though it continue for months or years, there may be no denouement that would rate the arching of a single weary eyebrow . . . no sudden and dramatic revelations such as are found in fiction, or in movie plots. And yet the analysis may be highly profitable to the individual, because of the accumulation of analytical "colors"—the myriad bits of infinitesimal knowledge; none dramatic in itself, but each contributing in its small way to the individual's complete understanding of himself and of his troubles.

One of the less dramatic things that I was taught to watch for during those Viennese studies was the progression of thoughts. For in free association, as Freud pointed out, one idea generally suggests another.

This principle is not difficult to understand, and may be easily observed in any group where smoking room stories are being traded. Mr. Higgenbottom's story about the Swede and the Mexican reminds you of the story of the Mexican and his burro. But even before you've finished telling it, you notice a happy expression spread across the face of Mr. O'Toole. And he shouts above the ensuing laughter: "You know, speaking of burros, that reminds me of this story about a mule, on a sheep ranch in Montana . . ."

The same type of association process goes on within the mind of the patient during psychoanalysis, but it is apt to be less obvious. And the analyst, carefully taking notes, wonders why the patient's story about playing hooky from school when he was ten years old, was followed immediately by a discussion of the argument he'd had with his meat dealer just last week.

But the progression of thoughts is only one phase of it. The analyst observes, also, the patient's narration of the argument. Does he acknowledge that there may have been two sides to the argument, and that the meat dealer had a point also? Does he reveal a feeling of contempt for a "mere tradesman"? Does he reveal a conviction that meat dealers and grocers and taxi drivers are all out to nick you every way they can? Does he indicate that such arguments with tradesmen are common in his life? Or that he was greatly upset for several days because of the incident?

And now, why does he jump from the description of the argument with the meat dealer, to tell of the time when he was sent away from the table as a youngster for not saying please? Is he uncomfortably aware of the fact that he wasn't polite, during the course of the argument? Does the meat dealer, because of his appearance, remind the patient of his father who sent him away from the table?

Then there are other things to be observed: Is the patient casual as he recites the incident about being sent away from the table? Or does he show traces of emotion, as if there were still resentment for that early reprimand?

He notes, particularly, when the patient commences to express a thought and then drops it quickly; is in a hurry to change the subject, or finds his memory suddenly growing hazy. Is there something here the patient is ashamed to say aloud? Is there some feeling of guilt he's never openly faced? Is this, possibly, something that's been bottled up too long in the unconscious?

Sometimes, as in the case of Mrs. G. with her daily attacks of asthma at four o'clock in the afternoon, it is possible to start an analysis with a definite hunch of what to look for. And sometimes, of course, hunches can be very wrong. In her case, we attempted to gamble on a short cut, by searching for memories that tied in with a four o'clock significance. And in her case, it paid off. However it should be noted that the analysis was not complete. We went searching into the subconscious to find the reason for the four o'clock asthma attacks and when we found it, we quit. If, two weeks later, she had started with daily headaches at ten o'clock in the morning, we would have been called upon to start all over. For reasons of economy and convenience, it was a limited exploration—like striking out to find Dr. Livingston, rather than setting out to explore an entire continent.

In the great majority of analyses there is no such dramatic clue and no such definite goal, and the entire dark continent of the subconscious must be explored.

During the exploration, the analyst notes any slips of the tongue, and he ponders the reason. For he couldn't be an analyst if he weren't a firm believer in cause and effect . . . convinced that nothing happens without a reason of some kind, hidden though it may be.

In this, he is no different from the engineer who believes there is a reason why a donkey engine periodically throws its belt or an electric motor eternally blows out its fuses.

When a man's wife is named Mary and he keeps referring to her as Helen, there's a reason for the transposition. But it's not necessarily what you think. It's the analyst's job to find the reason, rather than hopping nimbly to the most obvious conclusion.

I think almost everyone has had a few embarrassing experiences illustrating how thoughts in the back of the mind can reach out and trip the tongue, and bring forth the very words he'd resolved not to say. Some years ago, for instance, I used to make frequent hunting trips with a friend of mine who owned a farm far back up in the hills. He was an expert huntsman, a fine companion, a skilled woodsman. But unfortunately he was crosseyed. And it filled me with a combination of confusion and terror each time he sighted along the barrel of his rifle.

Ordinarily, I never used the expression "cockeyed." But in spite of anything I could do, it peppered my conversation when I was with him. "Honest to John, I'm so cockeyed tired of lugging this cockeyed rifle around these cockeyed hills, I don't think I can walk another cockeyed step." (That might be a slight exaggeration, but it didn't seem so at the time.)

Psychoanalysts have in a number of dramatic instances traced a slip of the tongue to some deep subconscious desire. And because this sounds like a refreshing variation on the old style mystery plot, a great many amateurs have seized it with enthusiasm. And widespread misunderstanding has resulted.

Many a woman who's read a little, and who's listened to tales around the bridge table, will draw down her eyebrows and sharpen her suspicions when she hears her husband make a slip of the tongue in idle conversation.

A young woman, reasonably intelligent and highly distraught, actually came to my office a few years back to ask what it meant when her husband announced that he was going to have to clean the Venetian blondes at his office. When I parried by asking her what she thought it meant, she spoke with remarkable conviction: "Obviously, it's some vicarious attempt at wish-fulfillment. He probably has designs on the blonde secretary in his office, and a subconscious desire to see her in the bathtub." Oddly enough, she could be right. But no long-shot player at the race track could ever hope for such overwhelming odds.

A very prim and proper young lady of my acquaintance was called upon, one Flag Day, to make a speech before a school assembly explaining the proper care of the American flag. At one point in her talk she was supposed to warn against wrapping and draping the flag. But she was horrified to hear herself announce, "The flag should never be dropped and raped."

To the layman, this might constitute prima-facie evidence that she held subconscious wishes to be overpowered and to enjoy a sex experience with a clear conscience, not having given her consent. Wish-fulfillment. Get it?

But unfortunately, psychoanalysis is not that simple. The causes of slips of the tongue and of spoonerisms and word transpositions may be many and varied. They may be inspired by subconscious fears as well as subconscious wishes. They may be artificially inspired by the conscious mind, or by the purposeful intent of another person, or by the lack of complete muscular coordination. There is, to my knowledge, no special psychological significance when a person says, "A big black blug bit a blig black blare."

One of the oldest tricks of actors, many of whom are still children at heart, is subtly to lay the groundwork for a transposition through straightforward suggestion:

"Look, old pal, in act two when you hold your head in your hands and say, 'This is a crushing blow'—just be awfully sure you don't say,

'This is a blushing crow.' That would sound silly, you know." And after it has been subtly suggested enough times, the final transposition on the stage is almost inevitable. Either that, or the poor harassed actor must pause in the midst of his dialogue and struggle to remember which is correct. And in either case, the amateur psychologist in the balcony could be thrown for a loop, attempting to tie it up to some subconscious wish-fulfillment.

Once the qualified psychoanalyst has noted a slip of the tongue, he has gathered a clue—but not necessarily the solution of the puzzle. He must methodically and definitely learn why the slip was made, or he must disregard it. The possibilities may be dramatic and exciting. The final solution may be trivial, and entirely irrelevant to the basic problem of the patient.

In detective stories, cigarette butts found at the scene of the crime generally help to track down the killer. In real life, they may have been tossed from a passing car and have no relationship to the crime whatsoever. And similar disillusionments are encountered in actual psychoanalysis, although they are seldom mentioned around the bridge table or incorporated into the plot of a psychological movie.

The experienced psychoanalyst, then, gathers an abundance of information about the patient through the process of free association. Rather elaborate and frightening terms are used in formal discussion of the process—"transference" and the "establishment of rapport" and so on. And to the average person, such terms may serve to confuse rather than to clarify. They endow the process with an aura of mystery which, in my opinion, it does not have. After a great many years of study and observation, I have arrived at the conclusion that there is nothing here more supernatural than goes on a thousand times a day when a couple of talkative women get on opposite ends of a telephone connection and give voice to every thought they can possibly drag in by the heels. There is only this subtle difference: The psychoanalyst is a trained listener, while the woman on the other end of the line is merely biding her time, a bit impatiently, waiting for her next turn to talk.

At one time, earlier in my career, I considered myself a fair-tomiddlin' psychoanalyst. And by the loosely knit standards of the day, I guess I was. I had studied under some of the best men in Vienna. I had acquired no professional or intellectual modesty that would cause me to doubt my qualifications to go joyously probing the unconscious. And besides, there was good money in it.

But times have changed since then. And possibly I have changed also. It has become less difficult in recent years to concede that possibly there are younger men who are better trained than I was, and who are more skillful in making use of their training. The psychoanalyst of today is a specialist in his own right. Psychoanalysis, early in my career, was merely one phase of a broad study.

The psychiatrists of my generation could be compared to the country doctors of their day—trained to set bones, remove tonsils, deliver babies, prescribe pills, and give lectures on public sanitation. The psychoanalyst of today is the product of intensive specialization. He is a doctor of medicine, with training in psychiatry; and over and beyond that, he has had extensive training in psychoanalysis. He has been psychoanalyzed himself—a rather nifty little precaution, like analyzing an antidote to make sure that it doesn't contain a heavy solution of the poison it's supposed to counteract.

When conditions have warranted it, and when budgets have been able to stand it, I have more and more in recent years referred patients of mine to some of the younger psychoanalysts. I am deeply indebted to my colleagues for their excellent work and for achievements which I know I could never equal. I will give them all credit and overwhelm them with genuine admiration. I merely reserve the right to consider some of their more intricate theories as poppycock. In more than half a century I have seen nothing to convince me that the psychoanalytical couch yields any peculiar psychic reactions, fundamentally different from those which occur in many different situations in everyday life.

Those of the Freudian school, particularly, insist that psychoanalysis is not really psychoanalysis, unless "transference" takes place—unless the patient transfers to the analyst those erotic wishes once directed toward the parents. It is necessary for the patient to relive his infantile sexual desires; and the analyst, being the only one handy, must round out the cast.

There can be little doubt that if psychoanalysis is continued long enough, the behavior of the patient on the couch will at times become peculiar. His recitations may become punctuated with emotion, and he may demonstrate a personal attachment to the analyst. It is somehow different from the relationship between a patient and the physician who is swabbing out his throat. And it was in an effort to explain and to classify this peculiar relationship between analyst and patient that the term "transference" was introduced.

But I believe I have seen a similar type of "transference" take place between a couple of drunken sots at the bar, sipping beer and making conversation far into the night. Their conversation, also, becomes punctuated with emotion; switching from tear-drenched humility and compassion for one another, to pseudo-sober hostility. Alcohol dissolves the inhibitions of self-imposed censorship and opens the floodgates of unrestricted conversation. As the words and thoughts pour forth they dislodge and emit an assortment of ideas and impressions that might otherwise be confined. These things stir up the emotions, and the alcohol is merely a verbal cathartic. Unrestrained conversation, whether on the psychoanalytic couch, a bar stool, or on a river bank during a fishing trip, is a purging process for the soul. There is nothing particularly mysterious about it.

Nor do I believe that the process of "regression"—of going back to relive experiences of the past—is anything unique or even remarkable. Any one of a thousand trivial incidents of every day can serve as the passport to send us flying back through time, to reëxperience some incident of the past.

Sometimes on a damp morning when the sky is overcast and there's a certain undefinable tang to the air, I will step out of my front door in Los Angeles, and onto a street in London. For a brief instant I feel exactly as I felt on a morning in England, long ago. For conversational purposes I may explain, "This reminds me of the weather in London." But in that first instant it is something more than a mere reminder. Even the old feeling of loneliness is reborn, momentarily. I am again a young man, far from home. A stranger, confused.

It doesn't last long. Perhaps in less time than it takes to blink the eyes, I am again an old man doddering along the sidewalk in Los Angeles and observing the morning dew on the grass. But the time element is not really important. Regression is a familiar experience to nearly all of us, so commonplace that we take it for granted. And we may fail to recognize it when it is singled out and dignified with a special name.

Such regression is quite common during psychoanalysis—and somewhat premeditated. Ability increases with practice, although some of the masters of regression have never had a lesson in their life. They're the older folks who turn their thoughts to the past and revert to the so-called "second childhood." Regression is not something mysterious, and unfamiliar to our common human experience.

With a ringside seat to your progression of thoughts which you have learned to express orally and without censorship, why shouldn't the psychoanalyst learn many things about you? He learns how you judge people around you. He observes your individual pattern of prejudice and your outcroppings of tolerance. He learns which traits you admire in others, and which annoy you.

He learns many things about you that you have never known about yourself, and for at least one very obvious reason: He is an impartial witness to your parade of thoughts, and he is capable of impartial judgment. You may be proud of your widespread interests, your eagerness to try new hobbies, your refusal to be driven into a rut, as are so many of your friends. But from his impartial viewpoint, all of this may show up as an inability to concentrate—an inability to tackle one thing and see it through.

You may, in a subtle and modest way, boast of your generosity. You may quote a host of instances where you gave until it hurt, and continued giving after that. But from his impartial seat on the reviewing stand, the analyst may see this as an inability on your part ever to say no.

Even your boasted chastity may appear to him as a basic fear of sexual intimacy, while your uncompromising honesty may hint of a conscience wound too tight. For he is a highly trained observer and he knows what's par for the course. He knows what's normal and what's abnormal.

And then before the analysis is completed, he enables you to see yourself as he has seen you. In effect, he invites you onto the impartial reviewing stand, to watch a play-back of the parade of ideas that has gone past. And he explains to the best of his ability, the meaning and the significance of all items of special interest.

The vast majority, of course, enter psychoanalysis with certain pre-convictions. And too often they are faulty. Prior to analysis, Irving T. informed me quite sincerely that he knew the source of his trouble. "I'm too easygoing, Doctor. I let people push me around, and then they start taking advantage of me. Finally, when I have to put my foot down—well—it creates a scene. I get all riled up, and I can't sleep." He was positive that if he could just learn not to give in so easily at first, it would avoid all the trouble that invariably came later. But during analysis, Irving T. came to realize that the "pushing around" he received was largely imaginary, and the outgrowth of suspicion; and that inversely, there had been little "give" to his nature. He had for years exploded at the slightest provocation, until he had lost most of his friends. He was an expert draftsman and had been steadily employed in a large industrial plant, but he was generally regarded as the hard-to-handle type. He had been blowing his top at frequent intervals for years; and, ironically, he had preceded each flare-up with the almost identical statement: "I generally let people walk all over me without saying anything, but this is one time, by God, when I'm not going to stand for it!" These incidents he had considered as "exceptions" to his otherwise easygoing nature. But during analysis he came to realize that his relationships with others, for many years, had been composed almost exclusively of "exceptions."

The patient's attitude toward the analyst during the first few interviews is generally revealing, for it is after all merely another human contact. An underlying desire for approval will be demonstrated by an extreme effort to please him. Hostile attitudes may be demonstrated by the eagerness to argue. "So I'm here, Doc, because my wife insisted on it. But I still think this silly hocus-pocus is a bunch of poppycock!"

These early attitudes aid the analyst in gaining an insight to the patient's social reactions and they are important. But if the analysis is successful, these early attitudes will gradually change. Elaborate, highly involved, and often fantastic theories have been offered to explain the peculiar relationship which develops between the patient and the analyst. In my opinion it is reasonably simple:

They build up between them one of the strongest bonds that can exist between two human beings—that powerful mutual association that belongs to two persons who have worked in unison to reach a common goal. And because of this, they learn to discuss the evidence impartially, and without reserve.

It isn't the father giving advice to the son. It isn't the master explaining the lesson to the pupil. No, it isn't even the physician offering his diagnosis to the patient. It is more like two tired fishermen, returned from the stream where they have fished for many hours side by side, discussing the events of the day just past, making their plans for tomorrow.

From the patient's standpoint, psychoanalysis is reasonably simple. In large measure, it consists of the oral expression of all ideas that flit through the mind—without reservation and without censorship. The most difficult task is to unlearn a host of early lessons in self-control.

From the analyst's standpoint, psychoanalysis is not simple. The techniques may be slowly learned but they are never completely mastered. It is an impartial review of often-baffling evidence. The physician may warn his patient to stop using alcohol and tobacco, and if he makes his recommendation sufficiently impressive he may expect a reasonable amount of coöperation. But the analyst gains nothing by warning his patient to stop worrying and to stop hating people. He must go beyond this to discover the basic cause of worry and of hatred. He must not only find these things, but he must enable the patient to find them also, and to appraise them. And he must teach the patient how to avoid them.

A man with an ulcer may arbitrarily be placed upon a restricted diet: "Eat no foods except those on this printed list." A man with a neurosis is not so easily regulated, and there is little point in suggesting, "You're to think no thoughts, except those listed here." The physician makes his pointed recommendations to the conscious mind, while the analyst must plant the seeds of basic preference within the subconscious mind. The physician may arbitrarily alter the diet, but the analyst must go beyond this to alter the mental appetite.

The significant thing is the fact that psychoanalysis works. It has worked. But during all my years of practice it has had its economic limitations. It is a slow, methodical, and costly practice; a one-customer-at-a-time proposition. It has occupied a position comparable to that of television, during the nearly two decades when reasonably clear and sharp video pictures were being telecast on an intermittent schedule, but when American industry hadn't yet been able to mass-produce receiving sets at a price within the reach of the general public.

There have come in recent years certain streamlinings of the psycho-analytic technique, and new promises of breaking the barrier, to make possible more widespread use of this previously restricted and expensive tool. Oddly enough, these newer techniques complete the circuit and return to the approximate spot where Sigmund Freud commenced his study of psychoanalysis, through the use of hypnosis. But an ancient road-block has been removed, with the development of modern hypnosis-producing drugs.

Here, however, we face something that has baffled more people than has Form 1040 of the Federal income tax returns. And no husband returning from a convention with ketchup stains on his collar has been more generally misunderstood.

I first met the mystery at a very tender age and it has served to keep me tantalized and a trifle mystified through a large share of a lifetime.

# 16

*We may take fancy for a companion, but must follow reason as our guide.*—SAMUEL JOHNSON

IN THE SUMMER of the year when I was nine years old there was wild excitement on the farm. Colored posters in town told of the forthcoming scheduled appearance of the Mighty Merlin, Mystic Master of Magic and Mesmerism. And for many days this was the chief topic of conversation among the farmhands. Even Chinaman Charlie seemed to catch the fever of anticipation and arranged to ride into town for the first time in years.

On the Saturday before the big event, I accompanied the rig as usual. And I stood for a long time watching the strange display in the window of Wampler's Furniture Store and Funeral Parlor. A husky farm lad sat astride a bicycle suspended in mid-air by an arrangement of sawhorses. There was a vacant, glassy stare to his eyes, as I recall. And he looked neither to the right nor left but stared straight ahead at the blank wall, pedaling methodically. In the window also was a small sign, and Uncle Charlie explained to me that the boy had been mesmerized by the Mighty Merlin.

Some of the people who had gathered before the window apparently knew the boy, for they tapped on the glass and called him by name. But there was no change of expression and no sign of recognition.

"It's just like he was asleep," Uncle Charlie told me in an awed voice. "He don't know nothin' what's goin' on; just does what the Mighty Merlin tells him."

After an hour or so of watching, I found my way back to the rig and curled up to sleep until the boys were ready to head back for the farm. And on the way home that night a first-class debate got under way.

"That guy in the window is just a fake," announced Big Ed. "I hid myself back of the watering trough by the blacksmith shop and watched him when there warn't nobody around the window and he couldn't see nobody on the street. And I see him get down off'n the bicycle and stand by the window, watchin'. Then when he sees somebody comin', he hurries up and gets back on the bicycle again."

For some reason, this announcement didn't sit well with Uncle Charlie. "You can't even see Wampler's window from up by the blacksmith shop," he announced emphatically. "Lease-wise you can't see good. You're just makin' that up."

Big Ed wasn't one to have his word questioned and it took the combined effort of everybody in the wagon to stop him short of mayhem. Everybody except Uncle Charlie, that is. Despite his seventy-odd years and hundred-pound weight disadvantage, he was all in favor of settling the question then and there with bare fists.

The upshot of it was that Big Ed and Uncle Charlie each bet a week's wages and we turned the rig around and drove back into town to settle it. By now Wampler's window was dark and the empty bicycle could barely be seen by the light of a kerosene lantern held up against the glass. But even Uncle Charlie conceded that it might be possible to see quite clearly from behind the watering trough that stood in front of the blacksmith shop.

"Anyhow it don't prove nothin'," he insisted. "They is guys that can mesmerize, whether this here Mighty Merlin can or not. Maybe he just writ ahead and hired this kid to put on the act, on account of he couldn't mesmerize him without coming here, personal." And on the long ride home Uncle Charlie recited fabulous tales of mesmerism demonstrations he had seen out in Ioway.

During the long summer evening of the week that followed, Uncle Charlie and I would often sit on the front porch of the farmhouse and talk of the strange power.

"They's something even better than mesmerism," he told me earnestly. "It's called hip'tism, and it's more newer. If I knowed how to do it, I could just look you in the eye and hip'tize you before you knowed what was happening. And then I could make you do anything I want you to do. Fetch water. Shine my boots. Haul the wood for the cook stove. Then when you come to, you wouldn't even know you done it."

This led to fantastic speculation and an orgy of daydreaming. During the long hours on horseback herding cattle, I'd envision myself as an accomplished hip'tizer bending men to my will. Chinaman Charlie I'd keep under a constant spell, baking pies and cakes and deep-fried bread dough for my daily delight. I'd hip'tize Big Ed and send him out to herd the cattle for me. Mr. Burton, the ranch foreman, would also have to come under my spell so he wouldn't object to such an arrangement. If I could just learn how to hip'tize, I figured, I wouldn't want for anything the rest of my life. With a snap of my fingers I could have the entire world at my feet, with all its people my slaves.

But Uncle Charlie was busy daydreaming also. And each night we'd get together and compare notes and giggle in delirious anticipation. The world was our oyster, if we could only learn how to crack its shell.

Two days before the big show at the opera house in town my father made one of his periodic visits to the farm. So freshly scrubbed and neatly dressed I went into town with him on the night of the demonstration and we sat quietly in the back of the hall. But I could see Uncle Charlie up in one of the front rows waving frantically when the Mighty Merlin called for volunteers from the audience. Uncle Charlie, however, was not chosen. Neither were any of the other boys from the farm. And I watched the remainder of the show with considerable misgiving.

During the mesmerism demonstration the volunteers from the audience wandered around the stage behaving strangely. At the Mighty Merlin's bidding they would bark like dogs, hiss like cats, play musical instruments, or make ardent love to up-ended mopsticks. The show was also replete with rabbits pulled from hats, women being sawed in half, and Mighty Merlin escaping from a trunk that had been locked and roped and tied.

On the way home I asked my father about it: "Is there really such a thing as magic? Could you really saw a lady in half and have her grow back together again?"

But my father shook his head. "No, son, there's no such thing as that. It's all based on tricks. Sleight-of-hand." And he demonstrated a trick he had learned, holding a coin between his thumb and fore-finger. When he snapped his fingers the coin disappeared. But he showed me how it had been sent flying up his sleeve.

"All magic is like that," he explained. "Sometimes you can watch closely and not be able to understand the trick, but you can be sure it is a trick all the same."

"Same with mesmerism and hip'tism?" I asked with false bravado. "Nothin' to 'em, is there? It's all just a trick."

For a long time my father sat idly flicking the whip at an imagined spot on the buggy shaft. And when he spoke, he spoke soberly:

"There are some things on this earth, son, that a man can't always understand. Some things you know are right. Some things you know are wrong. And some things—well—you just can't be sure. Sometimes you go through life never knowing quite what to believe . . ."

In the years that followed I shared that uncertainty; never quite willing to accept hypnotism as a fact—never thoroughly convinced it was all a fake. And then upon completion of my internship in the Boston Children's Hospital, I became associated with Dr. Morton Prince in Boston. And here, for the first time, I came in direct personal contact with the use of hypnosis as a tool in medical practice.

Dr. Prince at that time was not only an outstanding physician but he served as editor of the *Psychopathic Journal,* operated a clinic, and wrote a great many scientific papers on the phenomenon of the double personality—many of which remain among the more authoritative treatises on the subject to this day. His books remain an important part of the modern medical library.

In the early days of my association with Dr. Prince, I was little more than a glorified and overawed office boy, worshiping at the feet of the master. And I am afraid there was nothing very professional about my attitude as I watched his proficient use of hypnosis as a sort of social anaesthetic, while he probed the hidden facets of personality the better to understand his patients.

"There's nothing remarkable about hypnotism," he told me one day. "You don't think anything about it when you watch a young mother rocking her baby to sleep, do you? They're basically the same technique, only the rocking process is more familiar."

"That's a lot different," I protested. But he shook his head and smiled crookedly.

"Close your eyes," he instructed, "and try to imagine what it would be like if you were to observe natural sleep for the first time. I mean, suppose normal people didn't sleep; and it weren't familiar and commonplace. Suppose you were called in to see a patient who sinks into a coma every night. What would you make of it?"

Since this was a hypothesis I had never before encountered, I found it difficult to form an intelligent answer. So I just sat there with my eyes closed, while Dr. Prince rambled on:

"The only reason people don't think of natural sleep as some fantastic mystery is because it's so all-fired familiar to them. When a baby won't go to sleep, his mother picks him up and rocks him, and maybe sings him a lullaby, and he eventually goes to sleep even though he didn't particularly want to. In the operating room, we want a man to go to sleep so he won't feel the pain. But since he can't just drop off to sleep by himself and stay there, we give him an anaesthetic. Sometimes a man has trouble sleeping at night. He has insomnia. So we give him a sleeping powder. Sometimes I want to put a patient to sleep so I use hypnosis. One is no more mysterious than any of the others."

"Still," I protested, "all of those things are basically different."

Dr. Prince stretched his arms toward the ceiling, then clasped his hands behind his head and leaned back in his chair. "Yes, they're different," he told me. "But they're still peas from the same pod. They're artificially induced sleep. Let me tell you how it is: There's the same difference between natural sleep and hypnosis as there is between a natural birth and a Caesarean section. It's a different technique, but in the final analysis it achieves about the same results."

It was Dr. Prince who suggested that in order to understand hypnosis I should learn to perform it. "There's nothing to it," he insisted, "and you'll find it one of the most valuable tools of your profession. Besides, there's all the difference in the world between sitting here and talking about it, and actually performing it, yourself."

There arose, then, the question of finding a suitable subject. And while Dr. Prince was a cynical and hard-bitten man in some ways he maintained a rigid code of ethics. He did not believe it would be proper to turn over to me some unsuspecting patient who had come to the clinic in good faith. And he left it up to me to find my victim.

For weeks I studied the history and the nature of hypnotism and carefully appraised the persons with whom I came in contact, like a grave-robber greedily appraising the cadavers in the morgue. But it is not an easy subject to approach. I couldn't quite summon the courage to suggest casually to some old friend: "By the way, would you mind stopping in at the clinic this afternoon to let me see if I can hypnotize you?"

Because I couldn't muster the courage to proposition anyone else, my first attempts were centered upon one of my older sisters who still lived at home. But all attempts met with a total lack of success.

Sometimes after a long session with my sister, speaking to her of sleep and urging her to think of a nice soft pillow, I would find myself so heavy-eyed that I almost couldn't stand it. But her eyes would be bright and sparkling with anticipation, like a child who had been led round and round a circus tent without ever finding the entrance.

Dr. Prince shook his head when I finally got up courage to tell him of my failure. "It's very difficult to hypnotize someone in your own family," he explained. "It's particularly difficult at first, because your sister knows you have never hypnotized anyone. She has no confidence in your ability to perform it. Absolute confidence in the hypnotist is the very first step in the entire process."

Fortunately, at about this time Dr. Prince hired a young lady named Miss Osborne to serve as receptionist in the clinic. She was young, attractive, and eager. And apparently Dr. Prince's rigid ethics did not interfere with his relationships toward his employees.

"It's much easier to hypnotize someone the second or third time than it is the first time," Dr. Prince told me. "The first time, you have to overcome a lot of doubts and fears." And he suggested that I give him a couple weeks to work on Miss Osborne, at the end of which time he'd have her "conditioned" to serve as my first subject.

His methods were subtle but effective. He first managed to arouse Miss Osborne's interest in hypnosis through a casual discussion of the subject with her. And then he offered to hypnotize her, just to show her how it felt. Several times in the ensuing two weeks, entirely in the spirit of adventure, he had her submit to hypnosis. And each time after it was over he would explain modestly: "Really, I'm not too good at this sort of thing. But you take that young Dr. Fisher, now. He's a master at it. Why, in almost no time at all, he can hypnotize patients I can't even touch."

I was kept informed of all this as it progressed. And I think I rather enjoyed the wide-eyed respect I received from the receptionist each time I entered the clinic waiting room. But I experienced the most severe case of stage fright of my entire life on the afternoon when Dr. Prince told me the stage was set and it was time for my act.

It was nearly six o'clock and the waiting room was deserted. Dr. Prince had summoned Miss Osborne to his consulting room and he turned casually to me as we entered the door.

"Jim, I've been telling Miss Osborne about you. I've hypnotized her several times, but now she wants to see what it's like when it's done by an expert."

I tried to smile, but I'm afraid it must have been a sickly gesture. I went immediately into my rehearsed routine, softly telling her that she was sleepy—oh, so sleepy. And after a short time I managed to take a deep breath and to speak more crisply:

"Miss Osborne, you are to clasp your hands in front of you. Close the fingers. That's it! Now no matter how hard you try, you will find that you can not unclasp your hands. Do you understand? You will pull as hard as you can, but you will find that your hands will not come unclasped. You may try it now and see."

Miss Osborne promptly pulled and tugged until her fingernails were white but her hands remained firmly clasped while I stood over her bug-eyed with astonishment.

I'd carefully planned a number of different suggestions for the experiment, but my knees were weak and I wasted no time in sharply commanding her to come out of it.

Thus came the final answer to a question propounded many years before by the Mighty Merlin, Mystic Master of Magic and Mesmerism. Thus disappeared my last doubt as to the power and the reality of hypnotism.

Well—almost my last doubt. A few minutes later when Miss Osborne was slipping into her coat out in the deserted waiting room, I couldn't fight back the temptation to nail down that one lingering apprehension:

"Look, when you were struggling to pull your hands apart in there and you couldn't do it—were you really trying to pull 'em apart and couldn't you really do it? Or did Dr. Prince put you up to that, before he brought me into the room?"

A doubting Thomas will not relinquish his last remaining doubts without a final struggle. And surely one of the truly great mysteries of the world, surpassing anything in connection with the Sphinx or the hanging gardens of Babylon, is the question of how man could have lived so long and learned so little of the strange psychic phenomena best demonstrated through hypnosis; and how he could have preserved his doubts, even unto the twentieth century.

Here, in all probability, is the oldest tool of the medical profession. It was the stock-in-trade of the early medicine man. It was the fabulous "animal magnetism" of Franz Anton Mesmer. It has fathered a thousand fads for "miracle cures" and undoubtedly has helped to foster revolutions. It has become one of the most efficient tools of psychoanalysis. And periodically it has inspired some group or cult solemnly to claim "the miracle discovery of the ages."

Because words must have specific meanings, and because concise definitions must fit into the modest space allotted in the dictionary, we have taken a very limited view of a very broad subject. We have defined hypnosis as a state resembling sleep, induced by suggestion—and generally the mental image brings a picture of some Svengali-type character making eerie motions with his finger tips. But this is a very narrow viewpoint. It is as misleading as to describe love as that strange emotion which causes people to hug and kiss each other. Both terms could possibly profit from a broader definition.

The power of suggestion brings many things, aside from a state resembling sleep. And the peculiar process we have singled out to dignify with the title of "hypnotism" is but one facet of a complicated and interrelated series of psychic phenomena.

After my modest start in Dr. Prince's office, I continued to study and to practice hypnotism with a great deal of enthusiasm. But my association with the clinic was not such as to afford any great opportunity for experimentation. And I am afraid that my understanding of it was still extremely vague at the time when I undertook my studies in Vienna.

Here, however, there was opportunity without limit. Then, as now, it was a highly controversial subject. Sigmund Freud, after using hypnotism as the very starting point of his method of psychoanalysis, had washed his hands of it, and a number of his followers had done likewise. But there were others who saw in it great and untried possibilities, and to them I turned for enlightenment.

I felt, somehow, that in order to understand the phenomenon I should experience it. And I eagerly responded to the first call for volunteers from among our small group. I cannot say it was entirely without misgiving. And as I raised my hand, I felt a little as I had felt on an earlier occasion when I'd recklessly placed myself at the controls of a horseless carriage and had signaled the man on the ground to start cranking.

That first experience and a few subsequent experiences have convinced me of one thing: It is a far more intriguing phenomenon to watch than it is to experience. The hypnotic subject, like the strip-tease artist, may be the least entertained person in the room.

Several times since passing my eightieth birthday, I have gone along with younger friends to see some special stage show highly recommended, but running far into the night. And always the plot turns

out the same: Shortly after the opening curtain, somebody shakes my
shoulder and announces, "It was a great show, Doctor. Too bad you
couldn't stay awake to see it." And always it reminds me of that
wasted afternoon in Vienna, long long ago.

When the trance ended on that afternoon, I found myself in the
front of the room bundled up inside my overcoat, and I was asked to
tell why I'd donned it. But I didn't know. There was no slightest
recollection of anything that had taken place during hypnosis, and I
learned to my chagrin that nobody in the room intended to tell me
what I had done. I was merely instructed to try to remember, and to
report back any recollections that might come to me during the next
few days.

About a week later, when I was still totally in the dark, young Dr.
Joe relented. "It was the silliest damn thing you ever saw. Old
Whoozis said that you were cold—slowly freezing. So you put on the
coat, and flapped your arms, and blew on your fingers, and we could
even hear your teeth chattering. And then he told you that when you
woke up you wouldn't remember a thing that had happened, and
apparently you didn't."

It seemed to me, after that, that I could remember the sensation of
being extremely cold. But I could never be quite sure whether I was
really remembering it, or whether the recollection was the result of
suggestion by Dr. Joe.

That was the last time during my Viennese studies that I ever volunteered to be the subject. And I noted, not entirely without resentment, that none of the other students volunteered to follow my original
example.

Considerable time was spent (if not actually wasted) during those
early days, discussing the difference between hypnosis and natural
sleep. It is an interesting point, and many authorities insist that a
comparison between the two states will prove more confusing than
enlightening. But an incident during those early demonstrations in
Vienna illustrated the difference far better than all the arguments
tossed back and forth among us. An elderly gentleman, anxious to
pick up a small fee, had been employed to serve as a subject. But he

couldn't be successfully hypnotized because he would actually go to sleep while listening to the soothing voice of the hypnotist, and awaken with a start at the first sharp command. After a number of false starts, the poor old boy had to be by-passed in favor of a younger subject.

But then natural sleep is an equally fascinating phenomenon, which man has taken for granted through the centuries. Our general misconception may be due to a great extent to the way our language jumps to arbitrary extremes. Either a man is asleep or he's awake, according to the language of the street. And most of us, ordinarily, visualize a sudden dividing line between the two. This gives rise to many an argument when a wife accuses her husband of snoring and he indignantly retorts that he wasn't even asleep. Each is convinced that the other must have been mistaken, and neither realizes that both could be reasonably correct.

Actually, science has discovered in recent years that there comes a trans-cranial shift of brain waves in the last stage of dropping off to sleep—like a car shifting into overdrive. But except for this, both sleep and wakefulness are comparative terms. And here, as in so many things concerning the psychic side of man's experience, it is largely a matter of degree. The gradual transition from the deepest slumber to the greatest wakefulness follows a fairly set pattern; so much so, in fact, that the daily course of study in the public schools is generally scheduled so as to place the more difficult studies in the early part of the day, at the precise time when children are most alert, mentally and physically. Many surgeons schedule their operations for an early morning hour, giving themselves ample time to be wide awake and yet getting the task finished before the body has commenced once again to coast downhill toward lethargy and eventual slumber.

Hypnosis, we learned, follows a pattern similar to natural sleep. It commences with the hypnoidal stage, which is little more than a sense of profound drowsiness, artificially induced. This is the jumping-off place. And rare, indeed, is the person who has not experienced this first step toward hypnosis—not just once, but many times.

Have you ever listened to the monotonous click of the train wheels over the rails until you've lost all track of time? Have you ever watched a pair of hands flitting over a keyboard, or stared for a long time at a monotonous stretch of highway streaming toward you as you drive . . . and then felt a sudden urge to shake your head and glance at your watch, while you realize it's later than you think?

These things are all representative of the hypnoidal stage. And no person who has experienced them should doubt his ability to submit to hypnosis in some degree. He's already done it.

From the hypnoidal stage to the deep hypnotic trance is a matter of progression, but not everyone can make it. This is similar to the individual differences in the matter of natural sleep. Some persons can sleep soundly through the night while a three-alarm fire is battled and conquered just a few feet beyond the bedroom window. And others will awaken with a start, at the sound of the family cat stamping his feet on a mohair carpet at the other end of the house. Some people sleep more soundly than others, and that's all there is to it. Some people can be induced into the deep hypnotic trance while others cannot. And that, also, is all there is to that.

Fascinating, too, when you stop to ponder it, is our unique ability to sleep through an eternal bedlam of traffic noises on the street just outside the window—screaming sirens and tooting auto horns, and trucks rumbling past periodically all through the night. And yet we may awaken with a start at the most insignificant sound that is unfamiliar and ominous, such as the stealthy opening of a downstairs window.

I am quite sure Dr. Prince was correct. If natural sleep weren't so familiar and so taken for granted, we would all of us study the phenomenon with amazement, and find it very hard to believe.

Hypnosis is no less remarkable. And, in my opinion, it is no more amazing. Through its use, fabulous things may be achieved. But it also has its very definite limitations.

Among the subjects of our early demonstrations in Vienna was Freda F. She was a charming and beautiful young lady of Swiss origin, well educated, and she spoke a half-dozen different languages with equal fluency. This latter attribute, combined with her ability to reach the deep hypnotic trance in a comparatively short time, made her peculiarly suited as a subject. And she helped to finance her study of music by serving as a human guinea pig in our psychological laboratory.

In one demonstration which I attended, she was instructed to place her hand upon the top of a small desk. She was told that she would be unable to remove her hand, and that the desk was actually a stove which would grow increasingly hot until the pain was almost unbearable. Not only did she writhe in agony, but perspiration stood out upon her forehead; and her hand, atop the desk, became white at the points of contact. In other similar experiments, Doctors Paul Schilder and Otto Kauders record instances of success in raising actual skin blisters.

At another time, in a deep hypnotic trance, Freda was instructed to stand up before the class, remove her clothes, and place them in a desk drawer. (This, you understand, was all in the interest of science.) But regardless of any scientific significance, she would have nothing to do with the suggestion. And her determination to end the trance was physically visible.

This was another of Freda's many attributes. She was a modest young lady. A professional strip-tease artist or an off-season nudist would have perhaps followed the suggestion quite readily; but to Freda, the very thought of disrobing before the curious eyes of so many strange men was completely repugnant. This, in fact, had been the purpose of the demonstration—to illustrate that a person, even in a deep hypnotic trance, will not perform acts that are distasteful or repugnant to the individual.

In yet another demonstration, a young man was informed that upon awakening he would be unable to see a large desk until after he had actually bumped into it. Upon being brought out of the trance, he gave every appearance of being normal and rational. And yet, when he was asked to name the items of furniture in the room he named everything except the large desk. When he was asked to walk to the front of the room, he bumped into the desk while making no attempt to avoid it, or to shield himself from the blow. This was a demonstration of that highly peculiar situation known as the posthypnotic suggestion.

Because I was young, and literal-minded, and more than a little obstinate, I at first rebelled at the whole idea of a posthypnotic suggestion. I'd seen it, yes. But I couldn't quite believe it. Hypnosis I could accept as being no more fantastic than natural sleep. But the posthypnotic suggestion appeared to me as something with no counterpart in an otherwise familiar world.

Besides, there was a technical question that bothered me. If the subject couldn't see the desk, what could he see when he looked in that general direction? Could he see through it, and see the pattern of the wallpaper, beyond? That didn't seem likely. Could he see just a big hunk of nothing, roughly in the shape of a desk—giving the room the appearance of a jigsaw puzzle with one piece missing? And if so, why wouldn't he get suspicious and ask himself: "How come there's a big rectangular-shaped hunk of nothing in my field of vision?"

I brought these questions up at one of our nocturnal bull-sessions. And even though most everyone present laughed at my questions, none could answer them.

Truthfully, there were a great many questions as to the nature of hypnosis still unanswered in my mind at the time when I left Vienna and I found among some of the psychiatric pioneers a little of the same indecision and perplexity my father had expressed years before on the way home from the opera house, after seeing the Mighty Merlin.

The early use of the posthypnotic trance in psychotherapy can be illustrated by the case of John W. who suffered from hysterical choking and gagging spells at frequent intervals. He complained that at these times his windpipe seemed to shrink, as if someone were choking him. He could breathe only with extreme difficulty, and he explained that the choking and gagging seemed to blast open the passage again for a short time and he could breathe almost normally for several hours.

Repeated examinations by a number of different physicians had revealed no pathological ailment, no foreign growth in the throat, no physical abnormality. And so one afternoon in Vienna, he was placed under hypnosis. He was told that henceforth he would have no more of the choking and gagging spells and that he would not fear strangulation. With a little throat massage and hocus-pocus going on, he was informed that this special therapy was removing the complete cause of his old trouble, and that it would be impossible for it to bother him again.

During the days that followed, under observation, John W. suffered no more of his hysterical spells and was released from the hospital. And I believed, as did many others at the time, that here was truly the miracle short cut of psychotherapy.

But those of the Freudian school were pointing out, even then, that there are certain limitations to the direct use of the posthypnotic trance to eliminate unusual behavior habits. They argued, not without logic, that it was about on a par with giving the patient a sedative to relieve the pain, while making no real attempt to remove the cause.

In the case of John W., for example, there undoubtedly was some deep-seated psychological reason for his periodic choking and gagging spells. There was some reason for the hysteria which brought them on. There was possibly some deeply hidden fear of strangulation or suffocation. And this fear hadn't started by spontaneous combustion. With patience it should have been possible to track down the incidents which planted the fear in the first place—to expose the roots to the clear light of reason, and thereby destroy the entire structure of the neurosis.

It was this failure of the posthypnotic trance to get down to the roots of the problem, plus an inability to hypnotize certain persons which caused Sigmund Freud to discard the use of hypnosis after he had done much to establish it. And his repudiation placed hypnosis in a bad light for several decades. It was almost as if Ely Culbertson had repudiated contract bridge as being bad for the eyes, hazardous to the nervous system, and no particular proof of skill or ingenuity. And for many years the more faithful followers of Sigmund Freud refused to have anything to do with the use of hypnosis.

Had I been more the faithful type and had I been more deeply impressed during my days with the master, I perhaps would have followed their lead. But the dramatic possibilities of hypnosis tantalized me, almost as they had during those earlier days of daydreaming on the prairie. I continued to practice it during years when its use was controversial, at best. And I continued to read, and to study, and to ask questions of myself and of others. I clung stubbornly and at times illogically to the conviction that there must be some simple explanation beneath the seemingly incongruous phenomenon. And my one-track mind kept tossing back my unanswered questions from the nocturnal gab-fests: "If a man in a posthypnotic trance can't see a desk that's in the room, and if he can't see through the desk, and if he doesn't behold a big desk-shaped hunk of nothing to thereby excite his curiosity, exactly what does he see? How is this sort of thing possible?"

Fortunately for my own peace of mind, I have lived long enough to see hypnosis return from banishment and from exile, and to take its place amid medical respectability. And with the minds of many men turned in its direction, there have commenced to emerge a few answers to my long-neglected questions.

Ordinary hypnosis such as we practiced during those early days in Vienna is today, of course, becoming almost as obsolete as the horse-less carriages of that era. Special drugs and truth serums have equipped modern hypnosis with an automatic self-starter. The hours spent by Dr. Prince to get Miss Osborne "conditioned" for my first successful efforts at inducing hypnosis would today be unnecessary. A mild injection of an hypnosis-producing drug would take care of all that. And the person who has such drugs at his command and who has the authority to administer them is a hypnotist, per se.

But these things are merely modernizations of the method. Hypnosis, itself, has probably changed not one iota since the early medicine man gave forth with his plaintive and monotonous incantations while doing a jitterbug dance around a pot full of boiling buffalo horns—doing valiant battle against the "evil spirits"—and producing strange reactions within the wounded warrior bent double before the campfire.

The lateral boundaries of hypnosis have grown more fuzzy through the years, and we are commencing to realize now that it is not a single, isolated, and highly peculiar phenomenon produced by the "evil eye," but is merely a dramatic demonstration of suggestion-response.

I have sat at the bedside of my young granddaughter while she was asleep, and in a soothing voice that did not awaken her, I have quietly suggested that she should stop chewing her fingernails, because finger-nails are dirty and because pretty little girls don't like to have fingers that are sore and ugly-looking. And with nothing more than this, I have watched her rebel against and finally break a habit that had defied all the efforts of her parents. There was no hypnosis involved. (Pro-vided we are to cling to the dictionary definition of hypnosis.) The child had merely gone to sleep for the night. But in the days that followed, she found her habit of nail-chewing repulsive to her; and her response bore striking resemblance to the posthypnotic suggestion.

Meanwhile, measurable results have been achieved in acquainting students with a foreign language, merely by playing language-lesson records in the room while they sleep. And had I realized this earlier in my life I might not have entertained such unreasonable prejudice against students who fell asleep in class.

Practically any Hollywood wolf realizes that a young lady may become more amenable to suggestion after a few cocktails, and this fact perhaps does as much to promote the sale of alcoholic beverages as does all of the national advertising.

There is undoubtedly a relationship between the states brought on by hypnosis, natural sleep, barbiturate drugs, champagne cocktails, pep-talks, monotonous train trips, and a host of other things—even though the terms that designate these states may be widely separated in the dictionary.

The language that enlightens us may serve also to confuse us at times, by establishing arbitrary and artificial boundaries—so that the definition of terms may be concise and limited and non-overlapping. The one-world philosophy could apply as well to man's psychic life as to his politics.

# 17

*The years teach much which the days never know.*
—EMERSON

HAVING NOW SPENT something more than three-quarters of a century in the puzzled contemplation of hypnotic phenomena, and realizing that my allotted study period is all but spent, I think I have arrived for the first time at that spot where the assorted and often baffling revelations commence to fit a logical pattern. It is almost as if the author of Life had borrowed the formula from mystery fiction, pausing to explain the significance of the various clues as the story reaches its final chapter.

In simple terms, to approach an understanding of the nature of sleep, hypnosis, and the posthypnotic suggestion, we could perhaps do no better than return to our original illustration—wherein the conscious mind is portrayed as the busy executive of a local telephone company, and the subconscious mind is portrayed as the Chief Operator, out in the back room.

Obviously, any executive who's worth his salt is entitled to at least two weeks' vacation once a year. And except in extreme emergency, you won't find him at his desk after 5:00 P.M. It's a matter of principle.

Telephone service, however, must be maintained on a limited basis all through the night. And stuck up beside the switchboard is a small card with the boss's home telephone number on it. Beneath the number, in large letters and heavily underscored is the admonition: "Call only in case of emergency."

Similarly, the conscious mind knocks off for a good night's sleep and a well-earned rest. But the subconscious mind must remain on the job the whole night through, in order to operate the complex human body and to meet any situation that might arise. It must also use a certain amount of discretion in judging what constitutes an emergency, and when it's worth while to arouse the conscious mind out of its night's sleep.

There's the rumble of a bus lumbering past. There's the whine of a siren. There's a heavy truck, backfiring, and a dog howling off in the distance. All these sounds vibrate the eardrums at night exactly as they do in the daytime. All these reports come in to the subconscious mind. And all of them get appraised and shunted aside as of no particular consequence: "Shucks! No sense waking the boss to tell him that!"

But then comes a faint sound, barely audible . . . as if somebody were running a knife along a copper screen, or stealthily prying open a window downstairs. This report comes trickling into the subconscious mind, like all the rest. Only now the Chief Operator arches her eyebrows and reaches a hasty decision: "I think the boss ought to know about this!" The conscious mind is immediately informed. And just to be on the safe side, the Chief Operator steps up the tempo of the heartbeat, tosses in an extra dash of adrenalin, and gets the body prepared for an emergency in case this should turn out to be one. And almost before you know what's up, you're sitting up in bed, holding your breath, staring bug-eyed into the darkness and whispering to your spouse: "Listen! What was that?"

Hypnosis could better be compared to the boss's annual vacation, when his duties are temporarily taken over by a man sent out from the main office.

If the hypnotist is successful, he immediately takes over the job of the conscious mind and commences giving orders—which he more tactfully refers to as "suggestions." Usually, these suggestions are oral, and they reach the subconscious mind through the sense of hearing, rather than using the regular inter-house phones which usually connect the conscious and the subconscious minds.

This presents the first of a number of intriguing questions: If the Chief Operator of the subconscious is as shrewd as we've been led to believe—if she can carefully discern between the sound of a window being pried open in the middle of the night, and the sound of a squeaky automobile driving past on the street—then surely she should be shrewd enough to realize that the voice of the hypnotist is not really the voice of the conscious mind.

There is, so far as I know, only one answer: Obviously, the subconscious mind realizes all this, but is willing to go along with the gag . . . and provided the gag isn't carried too far.

Upon this point hinges one of the greatest controversies of the whole nature of hypnosis. But I have never, personally, heard any other explanation that I was willing to accept.

In a way, I suppose, the subconscious mind must get a little bored with its ordinary relationship to the conscious mind, with all its odd whims and ridiculous ideas; and possibly operates on the theory that any change would be a refreshing experience. The willingness to accept hypnosis might be compared to a subconscious yearning for alcohol, which likewise works subtle changes upon the conscious mind, and upon the usual conscious-subconscious relationship.

Under hypnosis, the subconscious mind may accept the suggestions of the hypnotist, not only as they apply to the movement of arms and limbs, but also as they apply to the various organs of the body which are under her control.

As previously mentioned, actual blisters have been reported when a subject placed his hand upon a desk top, with the suggestion that he was holding his hand on a hot stove. But the blisters were not produced by heat. They were produced by the body's effort to combat heat. The subconscious mind had gone along with the gag, to the extent that she'd called out the local fire department.

The Chief Operator of the telephone company, being a conscientious type of individual, may carefully check the boss's itinerary when he leaves on vacation. She knows where to get in touch with him at any time, in case the relief man can't keep the situation in hand, or attempts to inaugurate policies that are in violation of the union contract. She can, on short notice, get in touch with the boss and bring him flying back to the office.

Similarly, the subconscious mind can, at any time, end the hypnotic trance and place the conscious mind once again in control. At the time when Freda refused to disrobe in front of the class, her subconscious mind apparently decided: "Fun is fun, and I'm willing to go along with the gag, and all that. But this is getting out of hand, and I'm not going to play any more." And with that, the trance ended.

There is an age-old question as to whether hypnosis could be used for purposes of seduction. And the answer, apparently, is an evasive "yes and no." If the subject finds the suggestion repulsive and disagreeable, seduction will not be possible and the trance will end. On the other hand, if the subject finds the suggestion quite agreeable, she can no doubt be seduced. But as has been pointed out by many students of the problem, in such an event the hypnosis was unnecessary and represents little more than a waste of time and talent.

Around the same point has raged another controversy: Could a person be hypnotized and, against his will, be induced to commit a crime? And apparently the same rule holds true.

A professional pickpocket, under hypnosis, could no doubt be induced to go out into the street and pick pockets. He could probably be induced to do the same thing without hypnosis. But a person whose entire moral code is opposed to such conduct would not go along with the gag to that extent.

This is controversial. And upon this point, not all authorities agree. But in my experience, the evidence seems overwhelming.

In one well-known and frequently debated case, Professor L. A. Harraden related how the hypnotist first made a straw dummy and placed it in the bed of a professor at the school where the experiments were held. He then hypnotized his subject, gave him a dagger, and instructed him to enter the bedroom and plunge the dagger through the heart of the sleeping professor. The subject obeyed, plunging the dagger viciously into the straw dummy, while in a deep hypnotic trance. And this experiment was offered as proof that the most heinous of crimes could be committed under hypnosis, and that the subject was a slave without a will of his own, obeying the arbitrary commands of the master.

We may assume, of course, that the subject was not a calloused killer, and that stabbing a sleeping professor through the heart would ordinarily be contrary to his moral code. And here, again, we must reëxamine our premise: If our theory is correct that the subconscious mind is merely going along with the gag (provided the gag doesn't go too far), then why wouldn't it rebel at anything so heinous as stabbing a poor college professor who's innocently asleep in his bed?

Once more we must be careful not to underestimate the shrewdness of the subconscious mind. It is engaged in a game of play-acting. It is living and breathing its role in the drama just as the most accomplished actor or the most uninhibited child playing cowboys-and-Indians actually lives his part. And yet we may be reasonably sure that the subconscious mind is aware of the plot and conscious of the audience, and never completely loses sight of the pretense involved.

In this historic case, it is possible that the subconscious mind was one jump ahead of the experimenters, all the way: "Obviously, this is some kind of prearranged trick. The hypnotist wouldn't actually instruct me to sneak in and murder the professor, with half the student body watching and listening. I'll just string along with the gag a little longer, to see what's the payoff."

There is a certain lack of realism in all laboratory-controlled hypnotic experiments, similar to that of a magic show or a freshman initiation. There is the ever-present realization that things are probably not as they seem.

But the most convincing proof of this theory will be found not in the laboratory but in the records of the criminal court. To the best of my knowledge, there is not one authenticated case on record where hypnosis has been used to induce a man to commit a crime against his will. It would be unduly naive to suppose that the possibility has not been envisioned by some ruthless Svengali equipped with the "evil eye." Apparently such crimes committed under a hypnotic spell have occurred thousands of times in fiction, but not once in actual practice. And beside that significant fact, all other hypothetical theories seem to bog down.

On several occasions in recent years, and mostly for my own amazement, I have attended court trials where the defense has attempted to establish the existence of some "evil spell." My relationship to the case, in each event, was merely that of a spectator. In only one case did I volunteer to give professional testimony, but the defense offered was so ridiculous and it bogged down so completely that the defense attorney changed the plea right in the middle of the trial, and I was left with my little piece still unspoken.

And I have wondered several times since why an attorney attempting to offer such a defense wouldn't devote at least fifteen minutes of his time to an investigation of hypnosis and hypnotic technique, before going into court.

To visualize the posthypnotic suggestion, we must now move ahead to the time when the executive of the telephone company comes back from his vacation and returns to his desk. And business at the phone company reverts pretty much to normal.

Three days after he's been back on the job, the boss notices that the operators in the back room are failing to turn in their daily reports. And he proceeds to blow his top: "It's a fine thing! I go away for a couple of weeks, and the whole organization goes to pot! What's the matter with all you folks, anyhow?"

But the Chief Operator calls him out into the back room and directs his attention to a sign on the bulletin board: *"ATTENTION! ALL EMPLOYEES!* Until further notice, daily report sheets should not be turned in to the front office." And it's signed by the temporary manager who was in charge during the vacation.

So the boss half way apologizes. "I'm sorry. I didn't know that sign was there." But he angrily yanks down the notice from the board and continues to scowl most of the afternoon. And he wonders why nobody in the back room bothered to ask him if that temporary rule should be continued in effect.

In like manner, during hypnosis, the subconscious mind is given its posthypnotic suggestion which is not countermanded when the hypnotic trance is ended. The existence of this suggestion is unknown to the conscious mind which has just returned from vacation.

The eyes actually see the desk in the front of the room. But acting upon previous instructions, the subconscious mind fails to report the details to the conscious mind. This unorthodox and highly fantastic behavior of the subconscious mind is not really so lacking in precedent as I once imagined. It's almost identical with the behavior of the subconscious mind during sleep, when it fails to pass on the report to the conscious mind that another streetcar has just rumbled past, exactly on schedule.

Once the subject has bumped into the desk and he has become conscious of it, he is bewildered. He wonders why he didn't see it before. The hypnotist explains that it was an object of posthypnotic suggestion, and the subject nods his head. But still, he can't quite understand how he could have walked right into the desk without seeing it.

The conscious mind, ordinarily, doesn't too fully understand the subconscious. But then, how many bosses ever do really try to understand the folks in the back room? The typical executive would no doubt be embarrassed if he realized how many things his secretary knows about him, and about his habits and whims and moods and idiosyncrasies. And the typical secretary would perhaps be equally embarrassed if she realized how little the boss really knows about her, or has ever taken the pains to notice or remember.

And that, I'm afraid, is about the relationship between the conscious and the subconscious mind. It's the subconscious mind that does ninety-eight percent of the work. It's the conscious mind that takes one hundred percent of the credit. It's the subconscious mind that worries and frets over the conscious mind and tries to protect it from bad news and unhappy situations, and attempts to cater to its moods and whims and fancies. And it's the conscious mind that goes along from day to day, wrapped up in its own ponderous thoughts and impressed with its own importance . . . and only dimly aware that there are lesser, insignificant folks, flitting around the office.

There has developed in recent years a use for hypnosis in psychoanalysis far removed from the posthypnotic trance. It is used as a sort of psychic and social anaesthetic.

A man with an inflamed appendix could not lie quietly on the operating table while the surgeon goes probing and snipping through his innards to remove the cause of the trouble. The anaesthetic relieves him of physical pain and he rests more quietly while the operation is in progress. It is not only more humane and more comfortable from the patient's standpoint, but it is far more convenient from the surgeon's standpoint. He can perform a delicate operation with great precision, rather than attempting to perform it on the fly, like a frantic barber attempting to give Junior his first haircut.

A man with a deep-seated neurosis cannot lie quietly on the couch relating incidents that are embarrassing and painful to him. He will not admit openly to the psychoanalyst those things which he has never admitted openly to himself. And the psychoanalyst, too often, must learn about his patient not by what is said, but by what is omitted. Psychoanalysis becomes a prolonged and tedious and expensive technique.

Hypnosis, used in this way, may relieve the patient of embarrassment or self-deception. It detours a thousand road blocks set up by the conscious mind, by the book of etiquette, and by Mama's early instructions not to discuss personal problems with strangers. It enables the patient to relive experiences of the past and to bring out into the open deeply hidden reactions. It produces dream-like stage settings with push-button convenience. It enables the subject not only to recall forgotten incidents but actually to reënact the crime. It saves the psychoanalyst a great deal of time, and it avoids a lot of lost motion.

Henry H. was picked up by police officers at the home of a woman named Mrs. Henry H., who insisted that the man was a total stranger to her, and that she had become deeply alarmed by his strange behavior. In a state of obvious bewilderment and confusion, Henry H. was then taken to headquarters, examined, and released without charge—a victim of amnesia.

At the time when I examined him, he insisted that he couldn't recall a thing from his earlier life. He had awakened in a cheap downtown hotel, unable to even remember his name.

"I went down to the desk and looked at the hotel register," he told me. "They showed me where I'd signed my name the night before. That's how I found out I'm Henry H. I don't know why, but the handwriting looked familiar. I knew it was my own. Then I looked in the phone book, and I found the address of Henry H. I rode out there in a taxi and rang the bell. When this lady opened the door she didn't look familiar to me, but I waited to see if she'd recognize me, and she didn't seem to. When I started asking questions she called the police. I figured I might as well wait there for them. It's a hell of a thing when you just wake up in the morning and don't know who you are or where you are."

I inquired about his baggage, his wallet, or other identifications, but he merely shrugged.

"The police are working on that angle. I didn't have any baggage or any wallet. Just some change loose in my pocket. They're going to try to check a laundry mark on my shirt."

Leading questions offered to him led exactly nowhere. When I asked him to type out a short note he was able to operate the typewriter with ease. And, significantly, when I gave him a telephone number to dial, he dialed only the first initial of the prefix rather than dialing the first two letters as is necessary in Los Angeles.

Through these and other tests of habit patterns not affected by his fugue, it was possible to narrow down the field until we could reasonably assume that he was a fairly well educated man from a middle-sized American city, accustomed to driving an automobile with an automatic gearshift, and using cream and sugar in his coffee. It was a fascinating game of playing detective, and with the combined ingenuity of both of us, we soon had a pretty fair picture of his normal life, for it is interesting to note that the conscious mind is the only one that takes an unscheduled vacation during amnesia. Habit patterns and unconscious reactions often remain remarkably unaffected, and the subconscious mind remains on the job.

The only trouble with this narrowing-down process was that in the end, Henry H. could have been any one of some five or ten million American men who might fit the general pattern. The police, meanwhile, were checking the missing persons' reports, and the story of Henry H. was carried in the public press.

When no appreciable developments had occurred within several days, I suggested to Henry H. that he submit to hypnosis and he agreed to try it. Fortunately, he was reasonably easy to hypnotize and after several attempts he reached the deep hypnotic trance.

Through suggestion, he was able to recall the circumstances leading up to his amnesia attack. It was an involved and ugly story, concerned with finding his wife in a most compromising position with a slightly moronic young man he had hired as a gardener. He had secured a gun and hidden himself on the premises, resolved to kill them both if they should return. But after several hours of waiting he had decided to wash his hands of the whole business, to move to a different city and start life over. He had purposely destroyed all identification except the one overlooked laundry mark on his shirt. The name Henry H., which he had signed to the hotel register, had been a fictitious name made up for the occasion.

None of these things, oddly enough, did Henry H. remember after the hypnotic trance had ended, and the amnesia remained complete. His fugue offered remarkable convenience, going right along with his earlier determination to forget the past and start life over. The subconscious mind had clamped a padlock on the file cabinets of memory, enacting its role perhaps not wisely but too well.

It was necessary in a later session to fall back upon the posthypnotic suggestion. "After you awaken you will hear the word 'gardener'— and when you hear that word you will be able to remember these things from your past life."

Then, in casual conversation after the trance was ended, I mentioned something about the weather and the drying up of lawns. "My place at home is in miserable condition. You just can't depend on a gardener unless you're right there to watch him, every minute."

Henry H.'s eyes narrowed and he almost gasped: "Gardener! That's it! I'm getting it! We had a gardener! The dirty son of a ——" He stopped short, clamped his mouth closed, and placed both hands to his forehead. "Let me think! Let me think!" He shuddered involuntarily, rose to his feet and paced across the room. "I know who I am, Doctor. It's all coming back to me now. My name isn't really Henry H., it's ——" But once again his mouth clamped closed. "I've got to get off by myself, and think this thing through," he told me miserably. "You've been more helpful than you realize."

"You'd better check in with the police," I suggested as he left the office. "They've gone to a lot of trouble on your account, Mr. X."

He eyed me sharply. "Then you know who I am?"

I nodded. "And don't ever let anyone tell you that a man can't run away from himself. People do it every day, and then wind up in police headquarters asking for help to find their way back again."

Far more dramatic than this simple case are some of the things achieved in our military hospitals through the use of barbiturate drugs, and particularly pentothal sodium.

I imagine almost everyone who's ever had a general anaesthetic has been regaled with accounts of "Boy, you shoulda heard what you told the doctor, when you were coming out from under the ether!" For anaesthetics have a way of stifling vocal inhibitions and the patient is apt to express in words, without censorship, any thoughts that come to mind.

Pentothal sodium works the same way, only more so. It is, in effect, an intravenous invitation to hypnosis, making it possible for the patient to relive the nerve-shattering experiences which brought about the particular neurosis.

Having reached an advanced age before this technique became established, I have never personally performed it. But I have observed it, and I have been personally acquainted with cases where the technique has been used by others.

Through suggestion, combat veterans suffering severe anxiety may live again through the terrifying experiences that produced their anxiety. They may wince with pain, give voice to their innermost thoughts and reactions, express their fears and their conflicts, and reveal deeply hidden emotions which they have never honestly faced.

Reasonably typical is the case of Donald G., a combat infantryman who went through a series of major invasions in the South Pacific and who was returned to the States on furlough just a few weeks before the Japanese surrender in World War II.

He was twenty-four years of age when released from service and for a time gave evidence of being reasonably normal. But he could not readjust to the demands of civilian life, was unable to hold a job for any length of time, and would lapse into deep moods of melancholy. He was unable to settle down to a normal married life with the girl he had married shortly before being shipped overseas. He commenced drinking heavily, returned to the family home, and it was largely through the mother's insistence that he was taken to the hospital for observation.

Under narcosynthesis he was encouraged to live again through a frantic episode during his last active campaign. He described in terrifying detail the incidents of the battle, expressing his own reactions and emotions: "Them dirty God-damn' Japs! You can't trust the little sons-of-bitches! The only good Jap is a dead Jap! And you gotta be damn' sure he's dead! Don't take that little bastard, Mac! He'll stick a knife in your guts when you bend over. Look out! I'm going to let him have it!"

There followed sobs, and screamings. "Don't look at me that way, Mac! You just don't know! You can't trust the little bastards. Wait'll you've been out here as long as I have. Then you'll find out! I had to do it, Mac. They'll pretend to be wounded, and then they'll stick a knife in you. How the hell was I supposed to know he was really wounded?"

And then at another point in the narcosis, his language became strangely free of swear words, but the sobbing was similar: "I didn't go to, Dad. I wouldn't shoot a doe if I knew it, would I? I saw some branches, and I thought they were horns. I'm telling you the truth! Don't look at me that way!"

From these things emerged the story of emotional conflict. Under battle strain, Donald G. had shot a wounded Japanese soldier. The look of disgust or reproach in the eyes of a fellow infantryman had apparently touched off an earlier guilt-reaction caused by shooting a doe on a hunting trip with his father. The two incidents had become somehow intertwined in the same emotional pattern. And thus reenforced, they constituted a guilt complex that erupted in abnormal behavior.

Guided by this knowledge, it became possible for the psychiatrist in charge to steer Donald back upon a more normal emotional course—to realize that to err is human and that to forgive is divine. And that self-forgiveness can sometimes be the most difficult and the most divine of the lot.

There is yet another use of hypnosis in psychotherapy, and that concerns the unique ability of a hypnotized subject to interpret the contents of his dreams.

The hypnotic subject finds himself free from the confines of a host of acquired inhibitions and more capable of understanding his own subconscious motivations.

But that is a story unto itself.

# 18

*True, I talk of dreams, which are the children of an
idle brain, begot of nothing but vain fantasy.*

—SHAKESPEARE

SINCE THE VERY beginning of human history, dreams have held the fascinated attention of man. Belief in their significance has come in and gone out of style more times than has the bustle. And the slightly bewildered recitation of these nocturnal and apparently nonsensical dramas has surpassed even the weather as a topic of breakfast-table conversation. But still we know surprisingly little.

Possibly a benevolent God provided dreams for the delight and amazement of primitive man, who had no hope of living to witness television.

Possibly dreams are the natural by-product of a slipping clutch in our mental apparatus, when the mechanism is idling, but not com. pletely stopped.

Or possibly, as Freud contended, the dream was intended to serve as a Rosetta Stone, eventually to teach man the important language of the unconscious; to unravel the strange and hitherto meaningless hieroglyphics that make up the psychic side of man's nature.

But whatever the reason and whatever the purpose, we have reached that point in human understanding where it would be inexcusably naive to suppose that dreams are an entirely ad-lib phenomenon run off on the nocturnal sound stage without purpose and without direction.

Primitive men, believing in supernatural beings, assumed that dreams were somehow regulated by these all-powerful gods. Fatalists, believing in destiny, have assumed that dreams are regulated by that over-all power and may contain revelations of things to come. And psychiatrists, believing in the existence of a subconscious mind, have assumed that dreams are regulated by the subconscious. If they are taking a lot for granted they at least are not without precedent.

Just as a student in college may be expected to furnish his own books and just as a guest at a community picnic may be expected to bring his own lunch, so were we in those early days in Vienna expected to provide our own dreams for study, analysis, and dissection.

And this, for me, proved a greater handicap than one might imagine. For I had, all my life, been a sporadic and intermittent type of dreamer with an unusually slow early-morning pickup. Not only would I awaken with complete amnesia on an average day, but if I chanced to be sleeping in a strange bed it would take me an unbelievably long time to pry my eyes open and slowly figure out where I was and how I'd gotten there.

Day after day I attended the group discussions totally unprepared and listened with secret envy while others recited their fabulous adventures with Morpheus. I also gorged myself on all types of unlikely foods before retiring, hoping thus to provoke the dream mechanism. And at times I'd find myself so eagerly excited to see if I'd have a dream that I had difficulty dropping off to sleep.

Once, in embarrassed desperation, I offered for group consideration a highly involved and apparently nonsensical dream that had been recited at the breakfast table by a young lady at the boarding house. It was out-and-out plagiarism, for I offered it as a dream that had occurred to me But I noted with some interest that it was promptly analyzed in such a way as to fit the known facts of my own situation.

When I at last confessed that my nights were usually dreamless, I received little sympathy but was informed that my shortcomings were due to a lack of self-discipline. "Your trouble is not that you lack dreams. You merely make an inadequate effort to remember them upon awakening."

I attempted, then, an elaborate program of self-discipline, denying myself the customary orientation exercises upon awakening, during which I had always struggled to recall who I was, where I was, how I happened to be there, and what day of the week it chanced to be. Immediately upon awakening, now, I'd struggle manfully to recall anything in the nature of a dream, and it seemed to help. At first, I could recall only isolated snatches of a mixed-up dream sequence. But with practice I reached the point where I could recall the most involved and often ridiculous details. And only after I'd consciously and soberly reviewed the plot and fixed the incidents well in mind would I permit myself to consider the day of the week, and determine whether the day's duties demanded early rising.

Some years later I used this same type of early-morning discipline upon my young bride, and soon transformed her from an intermittent, hit-or-miss type of dreamer to a highly reliable seven-nights-a-week source of original dream dramas, all of which I reviewed like a Broadway critic run amock . . . until the morning of the revolt over the coffee cups.

But even in view of all these years of effort and experience, it remains my conviction that dream analysis will never be of any widespread value in psychotherapy. It requires too much study and training on the part of the analyst. The margin of error is far too great. It can never be done wholesale, but must remain strictly a one-customer-at-a-time proposition. Without a great amount of practice, the average person cannot remember his dreams with sufficient clarity to make an analysis reliable. And in these days when the average man no longer bothers to shine his own shoes and the typical housewife no longer bakes her own bread, I cannot go along with those optimistic souls who believe that the typical American can be taught to analyze his own dreams. Even if he could master the technique (which is quite unlikely) it would be only a matter of time until he'd want to hire somebody to do the job for him in a minimum amount of time at a minimum of cost.

And yet the great pioneering work that has been done in the field of dream analysis, and is being done today, gives us an ever-greater insight into the strange workings of the subconscious mind, and a fuller understanding of the psychic side of man's life.

Dream analysis is essentially a reconnaissance mission into the realm of the subconscious—well worth the trip for those who wish to grasp the lay of the land, but in itself no real triumph in the rugged battle to gain ground against the discomforts of mind and body.

The fact that dreams are influenced by our immediate physical surroundings should be reasonably obvious to anyone. Who, I wonder, has not dreamed that he was battling his way through a blinding blizzard, only to awaken and discover that his bed partner has stolen the blankets on a chilly night?

Who has not dreamed that he was falling over the brink of a chasm, only to awaken and find he's fallen out of bed?

These things offer evidence of the fact that the mind whips up a dream to accommodate those sensations being experienced by the body. And not merely external, but internal, as well.

I can recall with some embarrassment a dream that occurred when I was a youngster on the farm, a reasonably widespread type of dream familiar to many.

The farmhouse, of course, had no inside plumbing. The privy, of a type immortalized by Chic Sale, stood out back of the woodshed. And on winter nights when the wind howled across the prairie, it took considerable courage to face the long journey "out back."

On this particular night I awakened to face the grim necessity of such a journey. But the night was dark and the floor was cold, and outside I could hear the icy wind whistling along the eves. I lay there for a long time trying to get up the courage to move. And then, miraculously, somehow, I was "out back" and finding glorious relief.

But at that precise instant I heard a roar like an angry bull. I awakened amidst a warmish tide. And Uncle Charlie, my bed partner, was out on the icy floor, pulling his long woolen underwear outward from his body and screaming at the top of his lungs: "You dad-blasted idjet! Take mind o' what yer doin'!"

There are no set designers in Hollywood who can do such an efficient job of turning out a finished set, right while the scenario is being written. And I am sure that my surprise was equal to that of Uncle Charlie. I was startled as well as chagrined to find myself still in bed.

The human body, of course, is subject to many discomforts, and dreams have a way of magnifying things. The man who is slightly chilly dreams of freezing. The man who is just a little too warm may dream of being trapped in the midst of a raging forest fire. And the man who falls eighteen inches to the floor doesn't ordinarily dream of falling from a park bench or the bottom rung of a ladder, but far more likely dreams that he is plunging over the precipitous walls of the Grand Canyon. Dreams tend toward the side of exaggeration. And because of their magnifying qualities, there is some evidence that dreams can find their inspiration in minor discomforts not always recognized during the waking hours.

Thus it has been found that dreams of suffocation are quite characteristic of persons suffering from diseases of the lungs, even though the existence of the disease may not be known to the individual. Short, terrifying dreams, and frequent visions of imminent and horrible death are reasonably characteristic of those suffering from diseases of the heart. And so on.

There is always danger that the layman, grasping such isolated bits of evidence, may take the bit in his teeth and head off toward some distant conclusion. And I should possibly point out that last night's dream of suffocation isn't conclusive proof, in itself, of active tuberculosis. It may have been caused by getting the head under the pillow, or it may have been brought on by a stuffy atmosphere, or a cold in the head. Or the subconscious mind, prowling through the old files of memory, may have come across the recollection of a time when you were six months of age and got all fouled up in the blankets of your crib.

For in addition to providing a clue to the physical twinges, pains, discomforts, and conditions of the body, dreams also provide a hit-or-miss inventory of the things stored away in the file cabinets of memory.

To anyone who has honestly and conscientiously studied dreams, one point seems almost incontestable: The incidents of a dream are sketched according to the memories and the experiences of the individual. Man, at best, is a born plagiarist. And the seven basic plots of fiction are probably not greatly outnumbered by the basic plots of dreams.

There are many celebrated cases in history and in literature offered as evidence of the fact that solutions to weighty problems have appeared spontaneously in dreams. The inventor awakens with the answer to a problem that has been tormenting him for months. The composer awakens to recall a haunting melody heard in his dream. And the poet hurriedly writes down the lines that came to him, as in a vision, while he slept.

Do these things, then, indicate some mystical and supernatural connotation? Is our dreaming apparatus a sort of mental receiving set in tune with the infinite? Is there something here beyond the comprehension of mortal man?

Such stories give rise to such beliefs. But the fact is, I'm afraid, that these unusual dreams prove to us only what we permit them to prove. And our convictions may be in ratio to our gullibility.

The inventor who beholds the answer to a baffling problem during a dream is undoubtedly remembering a thought that had passed fleetingly through his mind at some earlier time and then faded completely from conscious recollection. And the composer who awakens with the memory of a haunting tune that filled his dream, may be amazed and embarrassed later to discover that it is remarkably like an older tune which he swears, in conscience, that he never heard in his life. And yet intensive investigation will no doubt show that he had heard the older tune years before, and that his conscious mind had forgotten it. Coincidence gets the credit for many things not rightfully hers. And it's little wonder that so many different songs have strikingly similar melodies.

Too often, also, the poetical hodge-podge that comes as a by-product of a dream sequence may be praised far out of ratio to its apparent worth, merely because the critics aren't eager to disparage the voice from "another world." And in the vast majority of cases even the dreamer, after his morning shower, may take a dim view of the ideas that seemed so colossal in the middle of the night. Only the exceptions provide the arguments.

In a celebrated and dramatic case nearly a century ago, a distinguished philosopher dreamed that he saw a small fern growing in a wall, and in his dream he knew the botanical name of the fern. Upon awakening, he looked it up in a botanical dictionary and was amazed to see a picture of the fern he had seen in his dream—and with the botanical name spelled out as he had dreamed it. He was not a botanist. He knew practically no Latin names for plants, he explained. Certainly he did not profess to know the highly peculiar names of rare ferns. And so here, it seemed, was proof positive that facts unknown to the individual can come to him in a dream.

It made a good story, and it stood up for sixteen years. But then, by chance, the same philosopher sat thumbing through a book in which he'd written years before. There, in the book, was a dried specimen of the fern he'd seen in his dream. And beneath it was the botanical name, carefully spelled out—in his own handwriting!

The details of the case are significant, for they help to illustrate the peculiar nature of dreams. As a younger man, the philosopher had written down the name of the plant as dictated to him by a botanist. It was merely an incidental act of courtesy, as he helped a young lady prepare a herbarium she planned to give to her brother. It was such a trivial incident in his life that it faded quickly from conscious recollection. Possibly two hours after he'd written down the name, he couldn't have remembered it at all. And yet years later the name returned with remarkable clarity in the course of a dream . . . illustrating once again the important premise that the subconscious mind stores away and retains memories not available-on-demand to the conscious mind.

At one time in my own life, I was deeply disturbed because I couldn't find an important paper that I needed urgently. I'd spent days pawing through desk drawers, and searching time and again through the same pockets, and delivering periodic lectures to the family to please, by George, leave my papers alone after this. And then, in a dream, I saw the paper folded up and inserted between the pages of a book I'd been reading. When I awakened, I found the paper exactly where I'd dreamed it was.

There was possibly nothing eerie or supernatural here either, although such an interpretation was instantly applied by many to whom I related the incident. The memory of placing the paper in the book had undoubtedly been in my subconscious mind all the time. It was merely my conscious mind that had forgotten.

Fairly illustrative of the dream process and familiar to most persons is the typical dream of embarrassment, critically studied by Freud and others. In this, the adult may dream that he is appearing in public with insufficient clothing. I, personally, on a number of occasions, have dreamed that I was standing upon a stage about to address an audience when, to my deep chagrin, I'd glance down and discover I'd forgotten to don my trousers. Invariably, I'd feel deeply humiliated, and attempt to leave the stage. And just as invariably, I'd be stymied for one reason or another. My feet would refuse to move. The curtains wouldn't close, or I'd find myself trudging futilely across a revolving stage like a man on a treadmill.

Oddly enough, there would be no jeers of derision from the audience; no ripples of laughter at my plight. My deep humiliation would be mine, alone, while everyone else appeared elaborately indifferent. All of these various factors combine to make the dream reasonably typical.

The "trigger" that sets off such a dream of embarrassment may be nothing more dramatic than becoming uncovered while asleep. Losing the blankets, or kicking one foot out from under the covers. That may set the "mood"—provide the journalistic assignment: "Whip up a dream about not being completely covered." But where does the mind get all these fantastic details about appearing in public without trousers?

Freud, in a number of remarkable cases, was able to trace such details to the early memory of the individual—and to an incident that's quite commonplace in the homes of our Western civilization.

Mama, possibly, is entertaining the ladies' bridge club when little Homer walks into the room quite unabashed, wearing his small sleeveless shirt, and having thoughtlessly left his training panties behind in the bathroom. He has no sense of shame. As a matter of fact, he has probably paraded around the house like this before without causing any particular disturbance. But this time Mama glances at him in horror, and dashes over to pick him up. She attempts to cover his nakedness with a scarf whisked from the piano. And even though she may not actually punish him, and even though little Homer may be highly confused by it all, still, in a hazy sort of way, he's aware that he's pulled a faux pas of the first magnitude. Here may be the very beginning of a sense of shame, and of acquired modesty.

The ladies of the bridge club, bless 'em, take it all in without any gasps or expressions of horror, and possibly try to place the distraught mother at ease: "Oh, for heaven's sake, Mabel, what does it matter? Leave the child alone. . . ."

Thirty years later, as a grown man, Homer may have no conscious recollection of the incident. But it's emblazoned indelibly upon his subconscious mind, and may provide the incidental action for recurring dreams. Only by this time, Homer dreams of himself as a grown man without his trousers, rather than as a baby without his training panties.

I attempted with only moderate success to find some such incident from the record of my own childhood, as a possible explanation of my recurring dreams of embarrassment. An older sister was the only one who could recall anything of that type, but she insisted that I was reprimanded by a woman employed in our home when I was about two years of age, because I wandered unadorned into the girls' bedroom when she was preparing me for my bath. I have no personal recollection of the incident and it was recalled by no other member of the family. But then, such incidents may understandably fade from conscious recollection. Surely, it is a far greater coincidence when such things are remembered than when they are forgotten.

Pertinent, also, is the fact that dreams frequently form about an incident that received no special attention from the conscious mind—a chance remark overheard several days earlier, or an insignificant scene from a movie that made no particular impression at the time it was witnessed. And the characters that flit through dreams are apt to be the most incidental characters from the world of every day—a woman casually noticed on the bus—a plumber who called at the house to repair a faucet three months earlier—a service station attendant in Albuquerque who fixed a flat tire on some vacation trip.

Through years of training, the conscious mind learns to appraise events as either important or unimportant. It is eternally busy with its evaluations and remarkably adept at snap decisions. But the subconscious mind offers little evidence of such acquired discernment. And a chance mention of the wholesale price of buttermilk in Oklahoma may be as indelibly recorded as the suggested starting salary on a job earnestly being sought.

There is considerable evidence that the ability to discern and to forget is largely an acquired technique, and that the familiar absentmindedness of old age represents little more than complete mastery through long experience in the fine art of forgetting.

Children have a way of amazing their elders with their unique feats of memory. Little Susie, aged five, may casually remark at the breakfast table that Aunt Martha had three buttons on the shoulder of her green dress, when she visited the family two years earlier. And later investigation may prove that little Susie is right. For months, the family may gaze upon her with awe, convinced that she's a genius. "Imagine that little tyke remembering such a thing! Why, it's fantastic!" But the truth is, little Susie hasn't yet mastered the process of appraising and forgetting. She hasn't yet learned to rid the conscious mind of irrelevant details, such as the number of buttons on the shoulder of Aunt Martha's green dress. The technique has to be acquired.

Extensive studies of older persons, on the other hand, have revealed a remarkable personal "convenience" in the things they remember and in the things they forget. In a state-operated institution, for example, the number of oldsters who get lost on their way to the dining room will be in inverse ratio to the quality of the meals being served. This doesn't mean that the old folks are playing a game or putting on an act. The appraisal of what to remember and what to forget may have become so fully automatic as to be beyond their control. It may be completely beyond their ability to find their way to a dining room that consistently serves cold mush and lukewarm coffee. And a new dietitian can do more to improve the situation than all of the memory courses ever devised.

So far as memory factors in dreams are concerned, there is some indication that the subconscious mind carefully skirts those topics that weigh heavily upon the conscious mind, when picking out the stuff that dreams are made of. For example, dreams of departed loved ones do not ordinarily appear at the time of bereavement when the waking hours are filled with grief, but may commence after many weeks or months have elapsed and the wounds have begun to heal. It is almost as if the Chief Operator of the subconscious mind carefully avoids messing around with the memory files currently being used in the front office.

Dreams, however, are not confined to the sleeping hours. In certain cases they splash out to include the waking hours as well, and we find an individual living in a world of strange hallucinations.

The psychoanalyst is interested in dreams, not as a reviewer or critic of the obvious, but as a student of the forces behind them. He might be compared to the movie mogul who returns home to contemplate not the plot of the picture he's just seen, nor the performances of the actors nor the quality of the cast, but to cogitate upon the production, and to ponder what a competing studio had in mind when it decided to film that particular story.

The psychoanalyst, then, is interested in dream symbolism. He may ask, "What did you dream?" But what he wants to find out is "Why did you dream it?"

Freud, with remarkable consistency, was able to find sexual significance in a great many dreams. An umbrella, for example, because of its method of erection and expansion, he interpreted as a symbol of the male sex organ. A ditch, a peach, an open gate—for reasons equally obvious—he beheld as symbols of the female sex organ. But it should be understood that he did not characterize these things as unvarying symbols, which could be written into a dream book, and applied with equal significance to all dreams involving umbrellas, ditches, peaches, or gates.

In fairness, it should possibly be pointed out that Freud denied—he did not author—the notion that all dreams call for a sexual interpretation.

The study of dream symbols is involved and undoubtedly controversial. It is apt to leave the general public more amused than amazed, and attempts to explain dream symbols are generally met with hoots of derision. And yet it is not so completely without precedent as the average person might imagine, for our waking hours are filled with symbols also. The wink, the grin, the friendly nod, the handshake and the clenched fist, the shrug of the shoulders—all of those and a thousand more, are really meaningful symbols of an underlying attitude or emotion.

I have observed enlisted men in the armed forces telling their immediate officers: "You are a pig-headed ass, and if you didn't have all that brass on your shoulders I'd tear you apart." Of course they didn't actually say it in so many words. All they said aloud was "Yes, sir!" But even so, they were able to express the idea quite completely and rather eloquently, just in the way they spat out those two words.

And similarly a lot of deep significance may find its way into a dream that has been "cleaned up" to pass censorship. For the conscious mind is eternally finicky about its diet, and certain basic notions drifting up out of the subconscious must be inverted or sugar-coated and disguised in order to be accepted at all.

From early childhood, the individual is taught that certain thoughts are "naughty" thoughts and must not be entertained. Other thoughts he learns to exclude because of bitter experience; they bring goose pimples, or insomnia, or restlessness. The person who has been made ill by eating contaminated kumquats learns to avoid that particular delicacy on the menu; and the person who has been made uncomfortable by entertaining morbid thoughts of death or deprivation, may learn to bar such thoughts from his chosen mental diet. Thus is established the process of censorship, and thus is born the need for symbolism.

The subconscious mind reviewing the routine reports from the eyes becomes aware of an attractive female off the port bow. She's wearing a rather thin dress, and there's a strong light behind her. The nostrils report a tantalizing fragrance. And with a commendable devotion to duty, the subconscious mind commences to prepare the body for the next logical act in the drama, keeping the conscious mind appraised of developments.

But all such erotic thoughts are turned aside as "unworthy" by the super-ego. They are "naughty" thoughts, and the super-ego is a trifle shocked. "Don't be silly! That lady is the organist at my church, and I happen to know she's very respectable!" And just to prove who's boss, the conscious mind under the direction of the super-ego embarks upon a sober contemplation of the preamble to the Constitution, while the blood pressure returns to normal.

The incident is quietly filed away in the memory cabinets. But possibly it turns up again when the subconscious mind is idly running through the records, picking out the raw material of dreams.

Obviously this entirely modest young man, confined by habit and a sense of propriety and rigid super-ego censorship, won't now dream that he sees the lady organist standing nude in the doorway of a brothel, urgently inviting him inside. By the time the dream is "cleaned up," he sees her in starched crinoline coyly inviting him through a garden gate that's all bedecked with roses.

But the significance remains, according to Freud. And if it remained, he was just the one who could find it.

Provocatively, a number of very good analysts have asked untrained subjects under hypnosis to analyze their own dreams and the dreams of others. And they report that many subjects demonstrate a remarkable understanding of dream symbols while in an hypnotic trance. Significantly, too, many of the same subjects were totally unable to do this when not under hypnosis, lending credence to the belief that hypnosis frees the subconscious mind of certain conscious inhibitions. The Chief Operator is more inclined to stand in the hallway and discuss office politics when the boss is away on vacation.

Through long practice, I have developed a certain amount of ability in identifying the various characters that stalk through my own dreams, and of tracking down the locale of each particular stage setting. Significantly, the technique works equally well in scrutinizing my daydreams, and my flights of imagination.

I have been an avid reader most of my life. And I discovered long ago that every written reference to a farmhouse invariably brought to my mind the image of the farmhouse where I lived as a boy. Sometimes, of course, it is necessary to do a little architectural remodeling. But it is a mental process, accomplished with no particular effort, and requiring no building permit. If the author of the story insists that his farmhouse has a pergola, and a giant-size fireplace in the kitchen, I efficiently add these details. But basically I can still identify the same old farmhouse, with the same room arrangement, and so on.

When I read of a boarding house, I can pause to identify the picture in my mind and soon realize that it's little more than a slightly redecorated version of the boarding house where I stayed while in Vienna.

The characters of fiction or history, also, take on identification with people I have known. I cannot, for example, picture Abraham Lincoln delivering his Gettysburg Address without hearing it in the peculiar though impressive monotone of my one-time friend, Dr. Beason.

The dreams of the night are certainly different from the dreams of the day—the guided flights of controlled imagination. But there's little doubt that they draw their props and their settings from the self-same warehouse. And a man can learn much about his subconscious attitudes by thoughtfully observing just which slightly altered characters from his own experience he casts in the assorted roles of heroines, villains, Milquetoasts, men of stern character, and women of loose morals. (Assuming, of course, that he is reserving the hero's role for himself.)

A patient of mine once told me with some concern that he'd attempted such association and he'd discovered to his amazement that in his mind he pictured every fictional woman of loose morals as a somewhat slightly altered vision of his wife. He was a man a little past fifty and his wife was in her early thirties. They had been married for seven years, and he had been married twice before.

In attempting to trace this subconscious attitude, he finally explained that in an erotic effort to compensate for a fading potency, he frequently encouraged his wife to recite the incidents of her earliest sexual experiences. These were not particularly dramatic, he conceded, centering around more or less normal childish curiosity and youthful exhibitionism. But they served to excite him. And they served also, apparently, to plant the seeds of unreasoned jealousy, and a subconscious classification of his wife as a sensuous and promiscuous woman, destined in his imagination to put on a modest disguise and to play the role of Amber.

It is significant, too, that this underlying attitude did not confine itself to the task of casting director for imaginary dramas, but unconsciously affected his entire marital relationship—even to the extent of influencing the terms of his will.

Such things as this, I have always found, are more readily accepted by the average patient than are the more involved revelations of dream symbols, although they are undoubtedly made of the same basic stuff.

During the days of my boyhood on the farm, before I had deciphered the mystery of the strange symbols which constitute written language, I was dependent upon others to interpret such things for me. Letters from home were always read to me by Mr. Burton, and in him I had implicit faith. But there were other times and other occasions.

Uncle Charlie, for instance, had his own odd little sense of humor. And sometimes on a winter's night he would smuggle Mr. Burton's copy of the weekly newspaper up to our room, and sit reading me items from the press.

"Listen to this! It says here: 'A whole bunch of lions and tigers and elephants is runnin' around loose, and was last sawn headin' toward the back pasture on Fisher's Ranch. These is all very fierce animals, and some of them is leopards which is the fiercest of all. They is also grizzly bears.'"

When I'd accuse Uncle Charlie of merely making it up, he'd manage to look hurt, and spread out the paper before my uncomprehending eyes. "I ain't sayin' it's right, and I ain't sayin' it's wrong. I'm just readin' you what's writ, right here in the writin'." And with a gesture of finality, he'd poke a gnarled old finger at some specific news item and invite me to look and see for myself.

"Show me where it says there are grizzly bears," I'd challenge. And with disconcerting conviction he'd point at a couple of words. "See them two words right there? Grizzly bears, they says. Just plain as anything."

Somehow I never quite believed Uncle Charlie. Not completely. In the dim light of the bedroom with the kerosene lamp casting flickering shadows across the ceiling, and with the wind furnishing mood music against the black backdrop of the night, many things seemed possible. But with the coming of daylight and the revelation of old, familiar scenes—then Uncle Charlie's news items seemed ridiculous and fantastic. And I could laugh.

In later years, when I've attempted to explain the deep significance of certain dream symbols to my patients, I've somehow felt just a little like a modern Uncle Charlie. I don't mean that I've purposely attempted to bluff or to deceive. But I've remained uncomfortably aware that nobody, as yet, has devised a method of checking the answers in the back of the book, to make sure that they're correct.

I've seen patients nod in semi-reluctant comprehension during the course of conversation in my office. However, time and again I've seen all belief fade in the bright light of the everyday world. It is apparent when the patient returns twenty-four hours later, that he's reached an independent conclusion: "That stuff we discussed yesterday was mostly just so much hog-wash."

But dreams, at best, are nebulous things. The day has not yet arrived when even the most qualified analyst can start with the oral recitation of a dream and work backward to sort and classify and identify the things which caused it. Dream analysis is merely one phase of the task, and serves as little more than corroborative evidence, supplementing the clues uncovered through free association, slips of the tongue, regression and guided recollection.

To the analyst, dream analysis is a reconnaissance mission over the distant landscape. At best, it can do little more than help to plan the strategy for the battle as it progresses. And the battle must be fought —and won or lost—right down on the ground, where the seeds of disorder are planted.

# 19

*Men of age object too much, consult too long, adventure too little, repent too soon.*—FRANCIS BACON

IF IT IS a sad thing to be a psychiatrist because you become uncomfortably aware of your own neurotic tendencies, then, I have discovered in recent years, it is a doubly sad thing to be an aged psychiatrist. For you may sit and watch the encroachment of senility with an abstract and almost professional attitude—like a surgeon watching the mirrored reflection of his own appendectomy.

At least once to every man, I'd imagine, must come the sudden and disconcerting discovery that the corporate cells of his physical body are rapidly approaching insolvency. The sand is running low in the hourglass of time. And the option has already lapsed on a thousand youthful dreams which were never brought to pass.

A fortieth or a fiftieth birthday can sometimes be an ominous thing for the individual who takes time out to think. Youth has gone. The eagerness of anticipation is slowly giving way to mellow recollection. Youth rides in the cab of the locomotive and jubilantly surveys the track ahead. Age rides in the observation car and gazes back with sweet sorrow, upon the fading scenes of the past. And it requires a certain amount of readjustment.

Somehow, it seems but yesterday that I was riding across the prairie with my two collie dogs. And now and then as I putter about the garden and inhale the fragrance of the good earth and the peculiar aroma of new-pulled weeds parching in a warm sun, I look up with tired eyes, half expecting to see a few old beehives standing amid the untrammeled orchard grass. Or to hear Chinaman Charlie beating out an unrhythmical tattoo upon the iron triangle that hung upon the back porch of the farmhouse, summoning the hands to dinner.

There are all the old familiar odors; there's the same warmth to the sun and the same depth to the blue sky. The fleecy white clouds drift lazily overhead just as they did so long ago, and the insects of the garden hum the same unchanged melody of contentment. And it is difficult to realize that I could have changed so much, amid a world of Nature that has changed so little.

And then, because I am a psychiatrist, I put those pleasant thoughts resolutely out of mind, and I strive from habit against those psychic forces which are struggling to complete the circuit and to return me to the days of my childhood and to complete senility.

My conscious mind is not ready for the retirement it has long since earned. And it struggles to maintain a certain semblance of office discipline, when the Chief Operator of the subconscious subtly suggests: "Let's just lock up the place, and spend the rest of our time sorting back through the souvenirs."

In a way, life is perhaps much more complacent for those who can quietly follow their inclinations, doing what comes naturally.

It is inevitable, I guess, that the highly trained swimmer and the lifeguard must struggle against the tide, even when there is no remote possibility of ever reaching shore. The training of a lifetime prohibits him from sinking quietly beneath the waves so long as he has the physical strength to take one more stroke, and even though he realizes that the waves cannot forever be denied.

And similarly, the trained psychiatrist, I find, cannot sink quietly beneath the lapping waves of senility, so long as he has the psychic strength to struggle against the inevitable.

I have in recent years discovered an almost overwhelming urge to revisit all the scenes of my childhood, to settle down quietly and spend my remaining days amid the once-familiar fields that echoed to boyish laughter. It is perhaps not so different from that mysterious lure which draws a salmon back to the stream where its life began. But for me, this cannot be. I find myself a full-time patient of an unrelenting psychiatrist who goes wherever I go, and who quietly vetoes the nostalgic dreams as they commence to form, and who offers substitute plans without resorting to oral suggestion.

And thus, in my eighty-seventh year, I find myself planning, not a trip back to Boston or Vienna, or Zurich, or Paris, or Chicago, or any of the places I have known in the past. Rather, my plans include a visit to Jackson Hole, Wyoming, and after that a trip up the Inside Passage to Alaska—two places where I have never been, and both of which have been described in glowing terms by others.

And these things I am afraid I would have to recommend to others who might come to me, as a psychiatrist, and ask how best to postpone the eventual encroachment of advancing senility: Don't sit in the observation car, with folded hands, gazing back upon the fading scenes of the past. Force yourself to seek new experiences, and to turn your eyes to the track ahead. Spend at least a share of your time, peering into the future.

But then if you should ask me why I recommend these things, or what is to be gained by them, in the long run—I'm afraid I couldn't answer. Possibly I, like old Maud, have developed a belated reluctance to follow the deep-worn trail along the last mile. Possibly my dimming eyes have lost sight of the glitter and the glamor of absolute normality as the only worthy goal of life.

But the aging process is not merely physical, nor is it merely mental. Nor is it a combination of the two, hitched in double harness. These things are so completely intertwined as to be inseparable and indistinguishable.

At about the time when the individual is gazing incredulously at the number of candles on his birthday cake and asking himself how so much of his allotted time on earth could have slipped away so quickly, there are certain physiological changes going on inside his body.

Just as the years of adolescence may be the most emotionally disturbed years of youth, so may the involutional period represent the most emotionally disturbed years of adulthood.

No one, to my knowledge, has been able to formulate any kind of sliding scale to determine just when the involutional period begins or ends. Roughly speaking, the inception may be found between the ages of forty and fifty-five for women; between fifty and sixty-five for men —with generous room in all cases for individual differences. It may end when the individual has found a certain benevolent philosophy of life and has made a concession to the inevitable.

During adolescence, Nature commences to turn on the physical and chemical and psychological forces of reproduction. During the involutional period, she commences to turn them off again. In both cases, the glands of internal secretion are directly affected and the body chemistry is altered.

There are many authorities who believe that schizophrenia finds its subtle beginning in adolescence, even though the ailment may not be classified nor even recognized until many years later.

To match it, the involutional period produces its melancholia—a relatively common type of mental disorder that is perhaps far more widespread than even the statistics would indicate. For in many homes, the most eccentric and erratic of behavior is disregarded with the whispered explanation: "She's going through the change." And involutional melancholia is apt to receive the attention of psychiatrists and statisticians, only when it has become extreme.

Here, too, the line between normality and abnormality is more than a trifle fuzzy. It is perhaps perfectly normal for a person of advancing years to ponder the things that might have been, to shed a few quiet tears over unclaimed opportunities, to sort fondly through the souvenirs in the attic, and to muster up a slight shudder at the grim specter of death waiting patiently, almost within view, at the end of the home stretch.

But when the feeling of depression continues, when the anxiety grows—when the individual becomes deeply preoccupied with thoughts of illness and of death, and when he is no longer able to find any consuming interests beyond the bounds of his own epidermis—then the outer limits of normality have been left far behind and the condition qualifies as a psychosis. Insomnia is common, as are delusions of guilt and convictions of failure.

Esther S., a married woman fifty years of age, was admitted to the hospital because of continued depression. There was no record of mental abnormality in her family, and her early life appeared perfectly normal. She was the mother of three grown children, and had always been known as a pleasant, happy type of person, somewhat reserved, but a hard worker with a deep sense of duty toward her family, her community, and her church. She had commenced with menopausal symptoms one year before admission to the hospital, and with the onset of the physical symptoms had come the deepening depression. She expressed feelings of guilt because of minor sex acts in adolescence, insisting that she would be tortured in the hereafter, and that her children would be punished because of her sins. Before and even after admission to the hospital she talked incessantly of suicide, which greatly alarmed members of the family, but there was no record of any actual attempts. In the hospital, Mrs. S. was given electro-shock therapy with complete recovery and had remained well for five years, at the time of my last contact with the case.

In my struggle to avoid melancholia and to keep interested in the game, rather than bowing gracefully to Father Time who holds all the trumps, I have striven particularly hard in recent years to keep alive a fading curiosity and to hold an open mind capable of admitting new ideas. This, in fact, is why I felt impelled to go traipsing off to Lima, Peru, at eighty-two years of age to study the progress of psychosomatic medicine. But that decision was easy to come by, because it concerned something big, and dramatic, and somewhat exciting. The most difficult part of the battle is to keep the mind from slowly going closed in the face of little and undramatic attitudes of every day.

Because my formal education came equipped with a delayed-action fuse and erupted quite suddenly during my thirteenth and fourteenth years, I found many of the familiar primary lessons of history unfolding in rapid succession. And from them all, I'm afraid I gained the impression that the masses of the world's people had done little of importance down through the ages except to laugh at men of vision. They laughed at Columbus. They laughed at Fulton. They laughed at Stephenson. And at the moment they were still snickering at Seward and his Icebox.

Later as I commenced my medical studies at Harvard I discovered the same hilarious pattern. They laughed at van Leeuwenhoek, Pasteur, Koch, Lister, Jenner, Harvey, and many others of an immortal legion.

And somewhere along the line I clutched at the germ of a basic ambition: I hoped that somehow I could steel myself to refrain from laughing, if Destiny should see fit to grant me a preview of some startling innovation. I hoped that I wouldn't be among those to laugh at some modern Columbus venturing beyond the world's previous horizons. And this, I find, is the most difficult ambition to retain in these closing years of life, in spite of a lifetime of practice. I believe I can truthfully say that never once as a young man did I ever stand on the sidelines and shout, "Get a horse!" as some venturesome soul went catapulting down the road at fifteen miles an hour in a horseless carriage.

I seriously studied under some of the great psychiatric pioneers of Europe at a time when derisive laughter could be heard quite widely throughout the medical profession.

I listened with an open mouth and an open mind when the first reports came trickling in about the Wright brothers' successful flight at Kitty Hawk. That doesn't necessarily mean that I believed the rumor. But at least I didn't laugh.

I prided myself in being among the first in our neighborhood to own a radio receiving set—a weird contraption with exposed coils, earphones, and an unfathomable probing device called a "cat's whisker," which skidded precariously atop the exposed surface of a chunk of galena. Not only did I own the instrument, but I was among the few persons to concede that the strange caterwaulings echoing through the ear-phones bore, at times, a remote resemblance to music.

However, this open-minded gullibility has left its black marks as well as its stars upon my record book. I once invested in the stock of a company that was going to produce self-bailing lifeboats, made possible through the use of an ingenious device that caused water to run uphill. And I am sure I have been considered a bit of a crackpot by some of my more stolid contemporaries who aren't so mortally afraid of being caught with their respective noses slightly elevated.

At one time early in my career I had an elderly patient who was urgently in need of a major surgical operation. But she was a firm believer in astrology, and she assured me that the signs were all wrong and that nothing but tragedy could result from an immediate operation. It would require a delay of forty-eight hours for the sign to become more favorable.

The surgeon whom I'd called in on the case practically choked when I explained the circumstances and asked if a forty-eight-hour delay would be possible.

"Ye gods!" he snorted. "You don't believe in that rot, do you? I've been a surgeon for twenty-five years, and I've never yet had to look up a patient's horoscope to see when it's safe to operate."

"It's not a question of what I believe," I pointed out. "It's a question of what she believes. If you put her on the operating table now, she'll go in there with the conviction that she's going to die. If you wait forty-eight hours, she'll be convinced that she's going to recover." But I'm afraid the distinguished surgeon was far from convinced.

"I'm not saying that a delay of forty-eight hours would be fatal," he conceded, "and I'll grant you that at her age we need everything possible in our favor, including her state of mind. But as a surgeon I'd have to insist that the sooner the operation is performed, the better."

We discussed the matter pro and con for some little time, attempting to evaluate the psychological advantages of a delay as contrasted to the surgical advantages of an immediate operation. And finally he conceded the point:

"All right, we'll go ahead and set it up for the day after tomorrow. But by God, I want it clearly understood that I'm opposed to the whole idea, in practice and in principle! When you give in to something like this, you're just helping to perpetuate a damned silly superstition. And we'd soon be in one hell of a mess if we had to start studying the stars, instead of examining the patients, to figure out what to do and when to do it."

Fortunately for the sake of my reputation and peace of mind, the patient recovered quickly and without complications after the delayed operation. But of course the question has remained open through the years. There are many patients who believe in many different things, and the shifting boundary between knowledge and superstition is subject to change either way, without notice.

Personally, I should always prefer the patient who believes something, as contrasted to the patient who believes nothing. Give me the patient who believes that a chunk of asafetida worn on a string around the neck will ward off disease, in preference to the patient who sits in complete resignation.

We may sneer at the ridiculous practices of the past, when surgery was a side-line for the town barber and when therapy consisted of little more than bloodletting. And yet many a service man who saw duty in North Africa during World War II, returned with strange stories of the practice of bloodletting among some of the unenlightened Arabs— and even stranger stories of recovery. But are they really any stranger than the stories from our own country, where a distinguished surgeon will have a higher percentage of recoveries at the Mayo Clinic than he will have after returning to his own hospital in Schenectady or Portland? He uses the same skills and the same technique, and possibly he has identical equipment at his command. But the reputation of the Eighteenth Street Hospital doesn't inspire so much faith as does the magic name of the Mayo Clinic in Rochester. And that makes a difference that can be measured in percentages, in the vital statistics column.

During the summer of 1950 I attempted to interest a younger medical colleague in attending a lecture at the Shrine Auditorium in Los Angeles featuring L. Ron Hubbard, founder of "The Modern Science of Mental Health"—Dianetics. I wished to attend, and since I have a nasty habit of dropping off to sleep as the evening rolls along, I felt it might be shrewd strategy to have someone in the next seat who could nudge me in the ribs at strategic intervals and possibly fight off the demands of Morpheus.

But my younger medical friend merely gasped and shuddered. "Don't tell me! You're not getting interested in that stuff, now?"

"I'm going to try to get interested," I assured him. "I've heard a great many rumors about it, and it offers the one thing I've dreamed of, all through the years—a chance to place psychotherapy on a whole-sale basis."

"But this Hubbard!" he protested. "Why, the guy is just an author of pseudo-science fiction. Pulp magazine stuff. No background."

"Pasteur was a chemist and not a medical man," I reminded him, with what I considered to be great dignity. "I don't know of any rule that says a writer of fiction should be barred from making any psychological discoveries."

"But the whole thing is preposterous," my friend persisted. "I've read about it, too. Just enough to know that I'm not going to waste a perfectly good evening listening to such tripe."

And so with a few parting comments about Columbus and Fulton, I reluctantly canceled the invitation and rounded up a nonprofessional friend to accompany me to the lecture.

I listened to Mr. Hubbard with, I believe, a reasonably open mind, and with hope born of desperation. But it seemed to me I could soon detect an old-fashioned recipe for his ultra-modern science: "Something old, something new, something borrowed, something blue."

The parts that were old and the parts that were borrowed gave little evidence of improvement, and the parts that were new were dogmatically stated without offers of proof or verification. (For the sake of my old-fashioned recipe, I am just arbitrarily assuming that Mr. Hubbard upon the platform, watching members of the audience walk out during the course of his demonstration, represented "something blue.")

The technique and the nomenclature, for some reason, reminded me of a psychic jam-session, what with individuals flitting back and forth along a "time-track" like a hep-cat getting hot on a slide trombone, accompanied by casual references to people who are "clears" instead of "squares." I rode home that night still wide awake, but sadly disillusioned . . . and, for some fabulous reason, recalling the meteoric but short-lived success of Franz Anton Mesmer.

In Vienna, at about the time of the American Revolution, Mesmer stumbled upon the Miracle Discovery of the Ages—the existence of "animal magnetism." It was every bit as startling as Mr. Hubbard's discovery of "engrams." To operate his "cure," Mesmer depended upon vast tubs, and bottles of magnetized water, iron rods, and elaborate ritual. To explain it, he introduced a whole new terminology, including such things as "great currents," and "pressures" and "final passes." To bolster his theory, he traced the course of magnetism down from the very heavens—in the form of meteors that left their residue in magnetized rocks. And for a time, tales of miracle-cures transpired from the consulting rooms. The lame could walk, and the blind could see. And the world watched, and wondered.

But soon Mesmer, himself, commenced to suspect that something was wrong with his elaborate and wonderful and foolproof theory. For he chanced to discover that he could duplicate his feats without the iron bars or the magnetized rocks or any of the usual trappings.

Men of later years were better able to appraise. What Mesmer had found was something that had never been entirely lost—the ancient art of the medicine man, better known today as hypnosis.

There've been others, too. Fads and foibles and faith cures. Sciences and superstitions, theories and therapies. And in certain cases, practically all of them have worked—in miraculous ways—for those who have believed.

And while I will admit to a certain weary sense of disillusionment after listening to Mr. Hubbard explain the engrams of Dianetics, still, I did not laugh. And to those who can successfully slide along their time-tracks and exorcise the devils out of their engrams and thus find a better life, I can wish only Godspeed and happy traveling.

There remain, however, other therapies, ranging all the way from the tepid bath to psychosurgery. And not all of them come equipped with explanatory theories. Shock therapies, in my opinion, cannot be adequately explained at the present time. They produce results in an encouraging number of cases, but there is no universal agreement as to why and how these results come about.

We have in our kitchen at home a very temperamental little radio that frequently ceases to work, for no apparent reason. Time and again we've sent it to the repair shop where invariably it plays beautifully. Its tubes have been checked and rechecked. But in spite of this it will periodically interrupt a breakfast-time newscast with a sudden and deafening burst of silence. And I have learned through experience that my long-neglected delivery technique will generally serve. If I lift the radio into the air and slap it sharply across the back a few times, it will commence wailing. And it may possibly continue working for several weeks.

I have patiently explained this technique to radio service men who come to the house. But they appear slightly confused, and assure me that there is no logical reason why this particular therapy should repair a radio receiving set. It is very discouraging and I would discontinue the practice, except for one thing. Usually it works.

And similarly, I believe, the fever and shock therapies in the treatment of psychoses have only one thing in their favor and that is the fact that they so often deliver results.

It has of course been known through the centuries that a change in the individual may bring about a change in his psychosis. That is where Father Time works his leisurely therapies. In addition, psychotic patients through the years have sometimes developed other ailments, such as malaria, appendicitis, influenza, dysentery, and so on. And while these things may have been inconvenient for the patients at the time, they contributed greatly toward new discoveries and the building of modern psychotherapy.

Julius Wagner-Jauregg, winner of the Nobel Prize in medicine in 1927, noticed that one of his patients recovering from malaria also recovered from his psychosis. And he pondered the possibility that the high fever may have brought about the recovery. He wasn't so concerned with figuring out why this could be or how it could be. He was grimly intent upon learning if it could be.

Not daring to experiment with schizophrenic or paranoid individuals, he tested his theory on two hundred victims of paresis—an organic psychosis which up to that time had been invariably fatal, and where the patients had everything to gain and nothing to lose through such experimentation. All were exposed to malaria and then nursed through to recovery. Fifty percent of the group recovered from their psychoses to such an extent that they could be released from the hospital and resume reasonably normal lives. No last-minute reprieve from the death house was ever more dramatic, and the therapy was not discarded merely because there was no plausible theory to explain it.

But the years have brought innovations. Malaria is still used, but in addition to this, the effects of high-fever may today be produced through radiant heat, or high frequency electrical currents, thus detouring some of the hazards of malaria itself. Man has learned to kindle fire inside the human anatomy, much as he once learned to kindle fire upon a primitive hearth.

But the fever therapy has never been found particularly successful in the treatment of functional psychoses. And in that field, other developments were taking place almost simultaneously.

A psychiatrist in Budapest, von Meduna, had been pondering the fact that schizophrenic patients seemed capable of developing many different run-of-the-mill ailments, but few were epileptic. Could it be that epilepsy and schizophrenia were incompatible?

He gave intramuscular injections of camphor in oil, to induce synthetically some of the symptoms of epilepsy, and thus to counteract some of the symptoms of schizophrenia. It is interesting to note that nearly a century and a half earlier, Weichardt had dutifully noted that camphor dosages were capable of producing vertigo and fits. But it is infinitely more interesting to note that when von Meduna tried it on his schizophrenic patients in Budapest he got results. Enthusiastic cheers went up throughout the psychiatric world, and schizophrenic patients everywhere took on a slight resemblance to second-hand pincushions. Immediate improvements were noted in a large number of patients and hopes soared high. But as so often happens, much of the original glitter faded as the facts were soberly pushed through the statistical mills, and the optimistic generalities were broken down for scientific appraisal.

Concurrently, a psychiatrist in Vienna was announcing a new system of shock treatment through the administration of large dosages of insulin, and this treatment appeared to stand up better under the cold light of statistical appraisal. Then, as in fever therapy, methods were introduced using electricity by placing electrodes on either side of the head and passing a carefully regulated current between the two.

Electro-shock therapy is not a pretty thing to watch, nor an easy thing to explain. Its use is justified only by the results it obtains, and these can be figured upon a percentage basis only. It is not a sure-cure and to my knowledge has never been hailed as the miracle discovery of the ages. If it is a miracle at all, it is a modest sort of miracle.

When other therapies have failed, and where there is compelling reason to believe that Father Time will not lend a belated hand in reducing the psychosis, there remains the possibility of surgical therapy; and particularly the pre-frontal lobotomy. Through a delicate operation, the surgeon partially severs the grand trunk line which connects the frontal annex to the rest of the brain. There is generally no reduction of intelligence. But, unfortunately, there is frequently a change in personality.

The frontal lobes, apparently, are a more recent annex to the brain structure, as man has become a more thoughtful type of animal with a higher forehead and a more preoccupied interest in destiny. They are, in effect, the "worry-warts"—serving somehow as the lookouts of the psychic process, staring into the future and reporting what's on the distant horizon of time. Those of us who worry a great deal about what's ahead are undoubtedly using the frontal lobes for all they're worth. As Voltaire pointed out, "We never live; we are always in the expectation of living." We're not interested in yesterday's news. We're not particularly interested in what's happening today. What we want to find out is what's predicted for tomorrow? After partial severance of the grand trunk line, the patient becomes more interested in the here and now. There aren't sufficient circuits remaining to carry on unlimited communication with the pre-frontal lobes, so the patient holds fewer grudges from the past, and he cherishes fewer dreams of the future. Unfortunately, he takes on some of the characteristics of the psychopathic personality—yielding to the temptations of the moment and not too deeply concerned about the ultimate consequences.

It is a drastic "cure," and is seldom recommended except as the lesser of two evils. Generally, the patient must be in such a sorry state that his conversion to a psychopathic personality could be viewed as an improvement, on the scales of comparison.

Rollo H., a giant of a man with chest and arms like a gorilla, was committed to a government-operated mental hospital as an advanced schizophrenic. He was syphilitic, and for years had been an alcoholic. Without warning or provocation he would attack nurses and attendants, and because of the tremendous power in his arms, he was extremely dangerous. He could not be prevented from urinating and defecating on the floor; and playing nursemaid to Gargantua might have been a pleasant pastime, by contrast. Incidentally, Rollo H. had carried the nickname of "Gorilla" prior to commitment.

After all other therapies had completely failed, pre-frontal lobotomy was recommended. It was no miracle cure, for the man remained demented, and there was no glimmer to replace the burnt-out light of recognition in his eyes. But he became reasonably docile and easy to handle. He no longer urinated on the floor nor soiled his person, although he will undoubtedly live out his remaining days in confinement. The taproots of anti-social rebellion and of ancient smouldering hatreds had been severed. A delicate surgical operation had achieved what could not be achieved by chains. And Rollo H., today, can sit on his bench in the sun, staring vacantly into space, rather than living out his days in a dark, evil-smelling, heavily guarded dungeon.

Interestingly, the perception of pain is generally reduced after pre-frontal lobotomy—for the advance dread is removed, and the magnifying glass of anticipation is out of service. In other cases which have been reported, drug addicts suffering excruciating pain during deprivement have demonstrated little evidence of such suffering after a similar operation.

These various therapies are undoubtedly wonderful things—all of them, from psychoanalysis to psychosurgery. Each stands as a glorious monument to the men who have dedicated their lives to study and research and experimentation.

But I can close my eyes and see the deep-lined face of my old-time friend, Dr. Joseph Beason. And it seems to me he shakes his head and announces sadly, "This is not the answer. You are winning a few isolated battles, and losing the over-all war."

For the great achievements in psychiatry to date have been like the development of new and ingenious tools for the body-and-fender repair shop beside the highway, while the accident rate itself continues to mount. Those who prepare the statistics for the United States Public Health Service must struggle with over-all figures nearly as large as those handled by the men who prepare the federal budget. They estimate that from twenty to thirty million American people are plagued by incipient or transient emotional disturbances. There are some five million psychoneurotics, the vast majority of whom will never see a psychiatrist nor visit a mental hospital, nor attend a mental-health clinic. But they will undoubtedly sow the seed of potential tragedies from Reno to Alcatraz. Approximately one person out of twenty will spend some part of his life in a mental hospital—and the ratio is kept that low simply because there isn't any more room.

Commendable efforts are being made to train more psychiatrists, to establish more clinics, to promote earlier and better diagnosis, to command more tax dollars and to build more hospitals—all of which are vital, but all of which are repair-shop rather than accident-prevention techniques.

# 20

*Men will wrangle for religion; write for it; fight for it; die for it; anything but live for it.*—COLTON

DESPITE THE FACT that my parents had been active church members for many years, there was little religious training in my early childhood.

During my father's periodic visits to the farm it was his custom to "say grace" at the dinner table. But at all other times the ritual was omitted. The farmhands arrived at the table freshly scrubbed and combed and, to them, eating was serious business. Conversation was largely restricted to one-word commands: "Bread!" "Butter!" "Sugar!" No time was wasted on idle chit-chat. And sometimes, with a slight touch of embarrassment, I suspected that the men mildly resented the small amount of time my father demanded for asking the blessing when he was present.

Uncle Charlie was an avowed Christian and a confessed sinner and a confirmed believer in the power of faith.

"If'n you had faith," he used to tell me, "you could go down to the crick and walk right on top of the water and not even get your feet wet." Once, inspired by his earnestness, I even tried it. But it didn't work.

"That's 'cause you ain't got faith," he told me sadly. "You say to yourself, 'I'm a-gonna walk on top of the water; I'm a-gonna walk on top of the water!' Only deep down inside, you don't really believe it. Anything in the world, a guy could do, if'n he just had faith deep down inside."

Big Ed, on the other hand, was a professed atheist. And at times he

269

seemed intent upon converting Uncle Charlie to his point of view. I'm sure Big Ed never knew it, and certainly I was too young to suspect it at the time; but I have often thought in later years that he was fundamentally a religious man who preferred to choose his own terms.

His most vitriolic abuse of the church came on the day after he'd attended a funeral in town.

"You know what it says right on the front of the stage there in church?" he demanded of Uncle Charlie. "It says, 'Suffer little children to come unto me!' I don't want nothin' to do with it, if it's got to make little children suffer!"

This, apparently, caught Uncle Charlie slightly off guard and he had to think it over a bit before offering any rebuttal.

"Well, maybe they got to suffer for their own good," he led off lamely. "Maybe it's like you brand a steer. Don't you suppose it hurts him when you poke him with that hot iron? Still, you got to do it so's to prove who he belongs to. That's like little children got to suffer, to prove they belong to Jesus." Uncle Charlie beamed triumphantly as he completed the illustration, but Big Ed was far from convinced.

"I wouldn't let nobody brand a kid of mine," he snorted. "Why'd he need a brand, anyhow, if'n he can talk? I don't want nothin' to do with it, if it's got to make little children suffer."

At other times Big Ed and Uncle Charlie would debate the questions of Creation and the origin of Cain's wife and the probabilities of eternal life. And while much of it went over my head I nevertheless listened with apprehensive interest. Quite often, it seemed to me, Uncle Charlie was on the defensive. And this chagrined me somewhat, for I always wished him to win.

I have often smiled in later years at the naive duplicity of Uncle Charlie and Big Ed, and their gross misconception of religious teachings, their ridiculous debates and their fantastic misinterpretations. But it has been, I believe, a tolerant smile, for I also recall that Uncle Charlie and Big Ed both lived long and useful lives, sharing a wholesome love for all living things, and accepting their respective roles with remarkable humility.

In the years after my return to Boston I attended church with reasonable regularity because it seemed to be expected of me. And I learned to look down upon the nonattenders in much the same way that I looked down upon those unenlightened barbarians who said "tomayto," and demonstrated a sacrilegious disregard for the sanctity of Boston culture.

Not until I took up the study of psychiatry did I pause to consider deeply the significance of religious ritual, and to ponder its value to the world. And it was a very sobering experience.

Religion had firmly established its claim as one of the three major contributors to psychoses, along with sex and insecurity.

I had learned that a sense of guilt or of shame lay behind many mental abnormalities, and I proceeded to examine many patients whose sense of guilt had obviously been deepened by sermons shouted from the pulpit, combined with awesome threats of hellfire and damnation. The negative philosophy of "thou shalt not," combined with fear and shame, seemed to offer little promise of relief in a world already overburdened with repression.

During those early years I examined many patients who could recite long passages from the Bible—but none who could honestly understand the basic philosophy of what he was reciting, and none who had lived in accordance with the rules being quoted. They were merely parrots, suffering from a peculiar type of parrot fever.

I have observed their kind, also, delivering funeral orations and conducting marriage ceremonies, and speaking parrot-fashion from the pulpit.

I have watched men and women take up religion for the same reason that they might take out an insurance policy: "It will be nice to have something to fall back upon, in time of sorrow."

I have watched others take up religion for about the same reason they might detour a black cat on Friday the thirteenth: "There's probably nothing to this silly business, but a person might as well be on the safe side, just in case."

I have seen those who embrace the church for the same reason that they might embrace a rich uncle: "Who knows? This may pay off, at some later date."

Yes—and I have seen the far greater numbers who drift into habitual church attendance for the same reason I did, long ago—because it seems to be expected of them. It is not a religious practice at all; it is a social habit.

I remember the deeply devout Mrs. Watson who lived near us, during our early days in Los Angeles. She was a self-advertised Christian, and the self-appointed custodian of the neighborhood's morals; in addition to which she would stop strangers on the street and demand to know if they'd been saved. And I recall the day when we were walking down the sidewalk and saw one of the young Watson children carrying a baby chick around the yard by the head, while it gasped and struggled to get free.

When the youngster failed to respond to our shouts, my wife dashed into the house to complain to Mrs. Watson: "Billy has a baby chick, carrying it around the yard by the head. He's going to kill it if you don't stop him."

But the devout Mrs. Watson smiled blandly and reassuringly. "That's all right. It was sick and going to die anyhow. That's why I gave it to him to play with."

And I couldn't help contrasting this with the bitter objections of Big Ed, who professed to be an atheist and who practically bubbled with indignation over the words, "Suffer little children to come unto me."

Yes, there were years then when I presumed to weigh the Christian faith, and all other religions—and to find them equally wanting. And I can say this without embarrassment today, and without apology. I fail to see how any person of reasonably normal intelligence could have reviewed the same evidence and reached any very different verdict.

But the years teach much which the days never know.

Possibly because of my earlier discussions with Dr. Beason, I could never be entirely satisfied with my role as a psychiatrist—struggling to find a safe pathway so that I might lead a few lost souls out of the wilderness of mental abnormality. Far too little was being done, I felt, to keep them from getting lost in the first place.

What was needed, I felt sure, was some new and enlightened recipe for living a sane and satisfying life—a recipe compounded from all the accumulated scientific knowledge acquired through study and research.

At one time I believed that perhaps even I could read and study and listen and cull and edit, until I had perfected an authoritative recipe. I dreamed of writing a handbook that would be simple, practical, easy to understand, and easy to follow. It would tell people how to live— what thoughts and attitudes and philosophies to cultivate, and what pitfalls to avoid, in seeking mental health. I attended every symposium it was possible for me to attend, and I took notes on the wise words of my teachers and of my colleagues who were leaders in their field.

And then, quite by accident, I discovered that such a work had already been completed. In fact, there are a number of such works, represented by the great religious teachings of the world.

For a specific illustration, I believe the following to be true: If you were to take the sum total of all the authoritative articles ever written by the most qualified of psychologists and psychiatrists on the subject of mental hygiene—if you were to combine them, and refine them, and cleave out the excess verbage—if you were to take the whole of the meat and none of the parsley, and if you were to have these unadulterated bits of pure scientific knowledge concisely expressed by the most capable of living poets, you would have an awkward and incomplete summation of the Sermon on the Mount. And it would suffer immeasurably through comparison.

For nearly two thousand years the Christian world has been holding in its hands the complete answer to its restless and fruitless yearnings. And it might almost as well have been holding a slab of Egyptian hieroglyphics before the discovery of the Rosetta Stone.

Here, and in other great religious teachings of the world, rests the blueprint for successful human life, with optimum mental health and contentment. But there are, unfortunately, many self-avowed atheists and many agnostics who refuse to listen. And there are many members of the church who are content to let such lessons form the structure of the Sunday sermon, convinced that religion has its time and has its place.

Man, unfortunately, is the product of how he lives. And a religion, to have purpose, must be more than a belief; it must be a way of life and a philosophy of life. It must be more than a form of divine apple-polishing, seeking special favor from the Almighty while here on earth, or in the hereafter.

Any man who has ever visited a mental institution must surely realize that the tortures of hell are not in the core of the earth, but in the very core of life. Here, too, is heaven. And also that vast purgatory in between, populated by those who have found neither overwhelming torture nor profound contentment—the lost souls ambling without purpose through their allotment of time.

For man, by his very nature, must have a purpose in life; an attainable and satisfying purpose. If he were a sheep or a cow, it might be sufficient to live from hour to hour seeking only food and drink and comfort. But eons of developmental heredity have endowed him with a certain mentality which must be put to some worthy use, or its very presence will destroy him.

An automobile, with reasonable care, may travel a hundred thousand miles or more, doing useful work and serving a definite purpose. But the engine of that car would run itself to destruction inside a hundred hours, if left running at full throttle, while the car stood idle upon the driveway.

And in much the same way, the inherent psychic forces of man must be kept in gear, to keep the body functioning with a worthy purpose, lest they run themselves to destruction in a minimum amount of time.

By long-standing tradition, by example and by instruction, modern man may find some challenging use for his intellect in the immediate pursuit of dollars. Social prestige follows closely the pattern of acquired wealth, and the culture money can buy. And the social register, in large measure, reflects the cold blue light of Dun & Bradstreet.

The man with a million dollars struggles as hard and grubs as deep as does the man who's almost penniless. But we possibly do him wrong, when we interpret it as greed. So long as he lives, he needs a purpose. He needs a challenge to his intellect, and a spur to his ambition. And the pursuit of dollars is the only purpose he has ever learned or recognized.

From a psychological standpoint, none of this would be harmful in itself if the final rewards were satisfying. It beckons a man from the mire of physical and mental indolence. But unfortunately it too often fails in the final test of satisfaction.

The simple, basic, and inescapable truth is that fear is multiplied rather than diminished by the acquisition of wealth. The more a man has to lose, the more he has to fear. And too much fear is a hazard to mental and physical health.

Daniel Boone, I'm quite sure, must have felt a type of self-confident contentment, as he strolled along through a primitive forest, for he was able to satisfy his needs for food, shelter, and protection—just from the materials at hand. Self-confidence is a major part of self-respect, and he entertained no doubt of his ability. A pampered millionaire, on the other hand, may feel completely lost and helpless in the midst of his lavishly furnished mansion on his butler's night off. The man who knows how to repair his own automobile experiences less uneasiness on a remote mountain road than does the man who has depended entirely upon garage mechanics. Even the advancing infirmities of old age cannot rob a man of self-reliance quite so completely as can money in the bank.

In establishing financial wealth and a higher standard of living as a worthy goal for our physical and psychic drives, we must inevitably lose the very things we set out to gain. In acquiring new wealth we acquire new fears. We acquire, also, a greater dependence upon others whose services we are able to hire. We confine ourselves within a tightening cocoon of inhibitions. We lose physical, social, and psychological independence in the pursuit of a will-o'-the-wisp ironically known as financial independence.

Back in the days of the Roaring Twenties, I took my family on a camping trip up along the Oregon coast. We lived in a tent, fished the streams, and combed the fields for berries. And we had fun. (Or at least we were under that general impression at the time.) And then just a few years ago I made approximately the same trip with my daughter and son-in-law. Only this time we stayed in motels and ate in restaurants. And the days were filled with apprehension, lest the night should bring an epidemic of No-Vacancy signs. Once when we stopped for a hurried glimpse of a particularly spectacular view, I chanced to find a wild blackberry vine beside a fallen log, and I called jubilantly to my daughter to come and share the reward. But she stood dubiously at the edge of the highway in her high-heeled shoes, and decided she didn't want to risk ruining her nylons.

And that, it seems to me, is a thumbnail portrait of progress, and the price tag of prosperity. The stomach can well afford to miss out on such things as wild blackberries. (They were a trifle green and more than a trifle sour, actually.) But the stand-offish, inhibited, and helpless attitude leaves its mark indelibly upon the soul.

Abraham Lincoln, we're told, once stopped his horse and rig to free a pig that had got stuck in a fence. And after that, presumably, Honest Abe was able to ride on down the road, modestly assuring himself that it wasn't anything any other red-blooded and compassionate American wouldn't have done. But his subconscious mind was undoubtedly impressed, and no doubt made its pleasure known in little feelings of contentment. "You know, when you come right down to it, Abe, you're a pretty nice guy at that!" Self-reliance and self-respect are two of the world's finest tonics.

A modern Lincoln, every bit as compassionate, would have to stop and think twice . . . provided, of course, that he could find room to stop beside the highway at all. "Let's see. It'il cost me a buck-and-a-half to get my suit cleaned, two-bits for a shine and ten cents for a tip, a quarter to run my shirt through the laundromat, and it'll make me two days late for my appointment in court." And by that time, of course, it's easy enough to decide that the man who owns the pig will probably come along soon and let him loose—and if the durn fool pig had any sense, he wouldn't have tried to crawl through the fence in the first place.

The great philosophers, the great thinkers, and the great religious leaders of the world, almost without exception, have warned of the perils of pursuing earthly treasures, and have earnestly recommended the simple life. Most historians have concurred, for the rise and fall of empires can be traced in the pattern of collective wealth and individual helplessness.

Personally, I am not discouraged. Man's groping for a better kind of life grows more frantic as he becomes more desperate. Simple truths cannot remain forever hidden. And a false position sooner or later becomes untenable.

For the first time in many years, people are turning in increasing numbers to the church. But far more significant are the changes taking place within the churches and the synagogues themselves, striving to teach people how to live instead of merely teaching them how to pray.

The rural shift of population in recent years, I'm reasonably sure, is indicative of man's restless quest for the reassuring hand of Nature and of God.

It is a subtle thing, but the basic lessons of the Scriptures are breaking their sonic barriers—finding their way into the books of etiquette, the codes of conduct, and the best-seller lists of contemporary literature.

But far more compelling than any subtleties is the grim specter of necessity.

It is mathematically impossible to sustain the projected curve with a continuing increase of psychotics and a spreading epidemic of neuroses, else eventually we should have so many people inside institutions that there wouldn't be enough left on the outside to run around and lock all the doors.

We can't continue indefinitely yearning for peace while anticipating war; groping for love while indulging in hatred; struggling for security while building insecurity. We can't live forever in fear of imminent atomic annihilation, lest that fear exact a higher toll than the potential bombs themselves.

Man will learn to live a simple and satisfying life, in harmony with himself and with his fellow men, because sooner or later he will have no other choice. And the hour of decision cannot be far distant.

He must learn to live a more satisfying life with less abiding fear, less nervous tension, and greater freedom from feelings of guilt and helplessness. He must find self-reliance and self-respect . . . or he must accept the already evident alternative: to surrender his intellectual superiority on this earth, through a process of reproducing the least intelligent among the population, and weeding out the rest through a spreading epidemic of abnormality.

We would have reason to question the wisdom of the poultryman who gathered all the eggs of his best-laying hens and scrambled them into omelettes, while setting the eggs of those hens with the poorest production records. And we surely have reason to question the wisdom of a way of life in the human species, where the birth rate is in inverse ratio to intellectual achievement.

It's been observed that the rich get richer and the poor get children. It's been ironically demonstrated that a sheepskin on the wall is the best guarantee against having an offspring in the crib. College graduates, on the whole, don't produce enough children to fill their own academic shoes. High school graduates do a little better. But the stork plays favorites with those who never went beyond the eighth grade, and who never waste the long winter evenings sitting around and reading Chaucer.

Intelligence and academic achievement naturally are not identical, but with the educational shaking-down-and-weeding-out process, they tend to run nearly parallel. And we've devised an ingenious system of thinning out the more intelligent strains.

I do not imply that this is bad. In the long run, it may be the answer to an only-too-apparent problem. Destiny, in her leisurely way, may give us a race of people who have less intelligence, less abiding fear, and fewer ulcers—a simple folk who can enjoy a quiet hour in the sun, who can look at the earth and find it good, and who can think of the future and find it promising.

The great trouble with modern man, in my honest opinion, is the unfortunate fact that he has forgotten humility. He has "gone Hollywood." He envisions himself as the unquestioned star of life's drama, with all the world a stage. The sun was created to dramatize his glory, and the stars are but footlights added for special effect. The "lesser" things of creation are but insignificant props to be used and cast aside.

Even within the human body, there sometimes appear certain types of cells concerned only with their own prosperity and the reproduction of their own kind. They conquer and destroy the other cells in a reckless program of exploitation, with no regard for the benefit of the body as a whole. If allowed to go unchecked they may kill, and eventually they perish themselves, amid the host they have destroyed.

Such cells we call cancerous. Medical science is striving today to find a way to control them, and undoubtedly a way will be found. And if man is to continue his reckless exploitation of the earth and of all the things upon it, then undoubtedly a way will be found to control him also. Perhaps our present mental and emotional instability and the lop-sided flight schedule of the stork represent the first subtle touches of Nature's patient therapy.

But it shouldn't be necessary to wait a thousand years for the cure. Simple humility should be within the grasp of any who will make the effort to reach for it, and simple contentment is the reward of those who can look to the earth and find it good.

Life is a changeable thing. The human body is like a vast civilization made up of individual cells. They come and go. They multiply and divide. They seek their substance from the stuff of the earth, and they return again to the earth. The same elements which composed a simple vegetable yesterday, help to compose the human body today. There is a kinship of all living matter, and an eternal flow of traffic, in the individual cells.

When a man can realize this, and when he can walk with humility through his garden and understand that he is but an integral part of the great coördinated drama of life and not the great star of the show ... when he can recognize a responsibility to contribute to a world he has learned to love, rather than attempting to exploit it to his own advantage ... when he can feel a bond of kinship toward all living things, including his fellow men ... then he may have found the key to contentment and the secret of a satisfying life.

The psychotic obviously does not love the world of eternal miracles which we speak of as the world of reality, else surely he would not strive to withdraw from it. And conversely, the individual who has learned to love that world, carries the strongest possible guarantee against becoming psychotic.

The child who has watched the miracles of new plants breaking through the earth in the spring; who has kept a silent vigil in observing a robin's nest; who has studied the stars and pondered the mysteries thereof; who has walked with Nature and talked with God, and stood in awe of the universe . . . has learned more than he'll ever learn from books. If he can retain his interest in the world, during those trying years of being polished on the grindstone . . . if he can look up to the heavens and down to the earth and keep his world in balance . . . he will surely be among the nineteen-out-of-twenty who will never spend time in a mental hospital.

This does not require any back-to-the-soil movement, nor is it an endorsement of the "simple life" as envisioned by Nature Boy. One man can climb to the roof of a tenement in the most congested district of the world's most congested city, look up at the night sky, and stand in awed humility. And another man can trudge along the fresh-turned furrows of the good earth, under a balmy sky, while his thoughts are completely occupied by the market price of spring wheat and the interest rate on his mortgage.

Nor is it necessary for a surgeon to pierce the skull and perform a delicate operation of pre-frontal lobotomy to bring us back to the here and now. By no more than a little self-control, a normal individual can cultivate the habit of seeking satisfaction in the present tense.

Five minutes of honest relaxation playing with a kitten and a piece of string can be a better therapy than a frantic trip around the world in quest of health. But in the stepped-up tempo of modern life, it's amazing how few feel they can afford to spend five minutes in such a trivial occupation.

We have cherished and preserved a host of couplets and proverbs from the past, intended to urge our more lethargic forefathers to get on the ball and get some work done. Things like Franklin's classics: "Dost thou love life?—Then do not squander time, for that is the stuff life is made of." And, "Never leave that till tomorrow which you can do today." We've preserved the stories about the grasshoppers and the ants. And in sundry and subtle ways we urge young and old alike to work faster and to squeeze each minute a little harder—to make hay while the sun shines, and to save up for a rainy day, and to anticipate the most horrible things for tomorrow.

Even though the nervous tension is mounting and the tempo of modern life is increasing and the casualties are falling like tenpins, we continue to quote the same old proverbs and to teach the time-honored lessons. And we are not unlike the man frantically screaming "gitty-yap!" to a team of run-away horses—because that's the only command he ever bothered to learn.

It isn't just a matter of proverbs, of doing a new needlepoint quotation to go in the frame above the sofa. But the proverbs and stories and quotations and morals—the commencement addresses and the routine editorials—all of these things and a thousand more have combined to build us a philosophy of life.

We've learned to abhor laziness, and to judge a man by the number of bathrooms in his home. We've been praised for our achievements and scorned for our failures. And still we crack the whip and drive the tempo faster, while the echo of one small voice lingers in the distance: the contention of the late Mahatma Gandhi that "there is more to life than increasing its speed."

Some years ago I made a trip back to the sprawling farm where I had been raised as a boy, and I sat most of the day watching the giant tractors pulling their gang-plows across the fields where once the cattle had leisurely meandered. They were ominous machines of rugged steel crawling relentlessly across the prairie and leaving a wake of neatly turned furrows. And that night at the dinner table I facetiously mentioned that one of these would be an ideal machine for a man who must bulldoze his way through city traffic.

But one of the drivers, an unimaginative soul, soberly explained that such a machine would soon pound itself to pieces on the unyielding pavement. "Without you put rubber tires on it, why it practically rattles your teeth out and jars every bolt loose, just driving the thing across the highway."

It seemed ironical at the time that a machine so ruggedly built for the grueling work on the farm could not indefinitely and triumphantly withstand every hazard that the city could offer with its precisely graded hills and its smooth highways. But it is similar, I'm afraid, to the far greater irony of human life.

Through countless eons, man has developed a rugged and an efficient body and a cunning mind, and a well-planned set of emotions, ideally suited for the struggle of survival in an earthly jungle. And then, in a comparatively few short centuries he has built himself a civilization. He has attempted to adapt himself to a way of life that is entirely different from that of his forefathers. Like the farm tractor pounding itself to pieces on the unyielding pavement of the city streets, he is rattling apart on the highway of progress.

Amid the rising crescendo of the eternal din, there comes a call for respite and a plea for some sort of pneumatic remedy to ease the jarring tension, as a crew of psychiatrists works frantically to tighten the loosened bolts.

Fortunately, the pneumatic remedy is ready and waiting—and has been since times of old. But it is not enough for man to find religion, and to learn to quote its text and say its prayers. He must learn the lessons the great religious leaders taught. He must take the lessons from the church and weave them into the warp and the woof of everyday life and build a philosophy as tightly woven as that of the work-harder-and-squeeze-the-minutes-tighter era. He must acquire a belated humility, but I am positive he will wear it well.

The human body, like the body politic, yearns for the peace that is contentment and the contentment that is health.